The Open University

Book 4
Energy saving in buildings

T206 Energy for a sustainable future

Prepared for the course team by Bob Everett and Horace Herring

This publication forms part of an Open University course T206 *Energy for a sustainable future*. Details of this and other Open University courses can be obtained from the Student Registration and Enquiry Service, The Open University, PO Box 197, Milton Keynes MK7 6BJ, United Kingdom: tel. +44 (0)845 300 60 90, email general-enquiries@open.ac.uk

Alternatively, you may visit the Open University website at http://www.open.ac.uk where you can learn more about the wide range of courses and packs offered at all levels by The Open University.

To purchase a selection of Open University course materials visit http://www.ouw.co.uk, or contact Open University Worldwide, Michael Young Building, Walton Hall, Milton Keynes MK7 6AA, United Kingdom for a brochure. tel. +44 (0)1908 858793; fax +44 (0)1908 858787; email ouw-customer-services@open.ac.uk

The Open University
Walton Hall, Milton Keynes
MK7 6AA
First published 2007.

Edited and designed by The Open University.

Typeset by SR Nova Pvt. Ltd, Bangalore, India

Printed in the United Kingdom by the Charlesworth Group, Wakefield

ISBN 978 0 7492 1865 2

1.1

Course Team

Academic staff

Godfrey Boyle

David Crabbe

Mike Davies

Dave Elliott

Bob Everett, course team chair

Ed Murphy

Stephen Potter

Janet Ramage

Robin Roy

Derek Taylor

James Warren

Course Manager

Karen Ross

Media Production Staff

Margaret Barnes

Sylvan Bentley

Sophia Braybrooke

Philippa Broadbent

Hannah Brunt

Sam Burke

Sarah Crompton

Daphne Cross

Claire Emburey

Clive Fetter

Alison George

David Gosnell

Rich Hoyle

Lori Johnston

Jo Lambert

Katie Meade

Lara Mynors

Lynda Oddy

Jon Owen

Deana Plummer

Andy Reilly

Jon Rosewell

Karen Ross

Mark Thomas

Howard Twiner

Consultants

Marcus Enoch

Martin Fry

John Garnish

Geoff Hammond

Horace Herring

Ben Lane

Stephen Larkin

Critical reader

Professor Martin Fry, Visiting Professor, City University

External Assessor

Erik H Lysen, Utrecht Centre for Energy Research, Utrecht University

External Examiner

Professor Tony Day, Southbank University

BBC staff

Anne Marie Gallen

Phil Gauron

Marion O'Meara

Contents

Chapter 1

Methods and techniques

by Bob Everett

I.I Introduction

The first two books of T206, Book 1, *Energy Systems and Sustainability*, and Book 2, *Renewable Energy*, have concentrated on energy *supply*. Cutting energy *demand* is equally important if large reductions in CO_2 emissions are to be made, such as the 60% cut by 2050 recommended by the Royal Commission on Environmental Pollution (RCEP, 2000).

Energy use is, of course, only the means to provide various **energy services**. The real task is to provide these at a lower energy and environmental cost. Book 3, *Managing Transport Energy*, has looked at the problems of doing this in the road transport sector. Here in Book 4 we look at energy use in *buildings*, which accounts for nearly a half of UK primary energy consumption. The energy services here include: the provision of comfortable homes and working environments, hot water for washing, hot food, safe chilled food storage, adequate lighting for homes and offices and the ability to use electronic equipment for communication, entertainment and writing books like this.

This first chapter describes a range of technologies and their application for making energy savings. Chapter 2 describes methods of testing and rating the energy use of buildings and the appliances used in them. These two chapters are specifically about **energy efficiency**; achieving the same level of energy services using less energy. There are many examples where energy use can be dramatically reduced. The phrase 'Factor 4' is sometimes used to describe the possibility of doubling wealth while halving energy use (Weizsacker et al., 1997). A more extreme version of this is 'Factor 10', implying a tenfold increase in energy efficiency.

Energy can also be saved through **energy conservation**, making do with a lower standard of energy services, for example by turning down winter heating thermostats, or turning off unneccessary lights and appliances. The question of what level of energy services are actually necessary is discussed in Chapter 3. It also looks at government policies for encouraging energy saving and some of the problems that arise in implementing them. Although this book concentrates on the UK, the technologies and methodologies are likely to be applicable in many countries.

The patterns of energy use in the UK were introduced in Chapter 3 of Book 1. A key diagram, repeated here as Figure 1.1, shows the breakdown of primary and delivered energy for the year 2000. This pattern is still much the same at the time of writing (July 2006).

Of the energy use in buildings 64% was in the domestic sector, 27% in the services sector and 9% in industrial buildings. Within the domestic sector there is a familiar range of energy uses (see Figure 1.2). In 2004 over 60% of delivered energy was used for space heating. The services sector contains a wide range of different buildings such as offices, schools, shops and hospitals. Although just over a half of the delivered energy was used for space heating, this sector uses large amounts of electricity, particularly for lighting (see Figure 1.3); in the retail sub-sector nearly 30% of the energy use was for lighting.

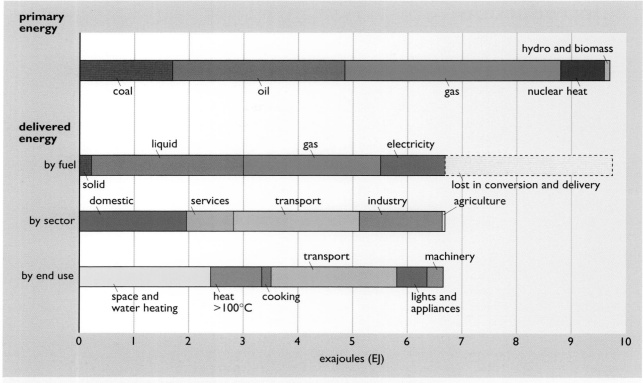

Figure 1.1 UK primary and delivered energy use for 2000 (sources DTI, 2001, 2006b)

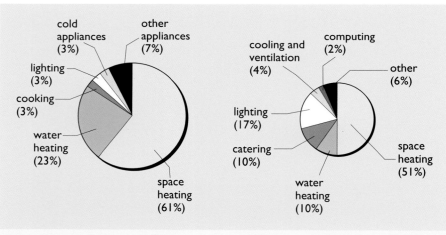

Figure 1.2 UK domestic sector energy consumption by end use, 2004 – total 2.0 EJ (Source DTI, 2006a)

Figure 1.3 UK services sector energy consumption by end use, 2004 – total 0.8 EJ (Source DTI, 2006a)

For each of the basic energy uses there is a range of technologies that could be used to reduce demand. Table 1.1 summarises the main topics discussed in the next three sections. The chapter then concludes with a discussion of the overall potential for UK demand reduction that is achievable by using these technologies.

Table I.I Reducing energy consumption in buildings

Energy use	Technologies for reduced consumption	Chapter I section
Space and water heating	Insulation; improved airtightness of buildings; ventilation heat recovery	1.2 Reducing space heating demand
	Increased boiler efficiency; improved heating controls; use of heat pumps or combined heat and power generation (CHP)	1.3 Improving heating system efficiency
Electrical and electronic systems	Avoidance of 'standby' wastage; more efficient TVs and kitchen appliances	1.4 Reducing electricity demand
Lighting	Use of daylight; more efficient lamps; use of efficient luminaires	
Ventilation and air conditioning	Use of natural ventilation; improved fan design and sizing; improved design, sizing and control of electric motors	

1.2 Reducing space heating demand

Heat energy is used in houses and offices for 'space heating', i.e. keeping the spaces of buildings at a comfortable temperature, and water heating, the provision of hot water for washing. There is a related topic of keeping buildings cool in summer. This increasingly is being carried out by electrically powered air-conditioning plant, so will be dealt with later.

A little history

As pointed out in Book 1, Chapter 3, life indoors in the past in the UK must have been very cold in winter. Houses in the 19th and early 20th centuries had a central fire (usually fuelled by coal), often also used for cooking and water heating, and were lit with either oil or gas lamps. They had to be well ventilated both to supply the combustion air for the fire and to get rid of the fumes from the lamps. The basic principle of keeping warm seems to have been to wear lots of clothes, sit as close as possible to the fire during the day and retreat under a thick pile of blankets in bed at night. In the 19th century offices did introduce the relative luxury of central heating, fed from large coal-fired boilers.

UK building standards improved slowly throughout the 20th century. In the 1920s cavity walls (an air gap between two separate skins of brick) were introduced, largely as a method to prevent damp penetration. The coal fire remained the normal mode of heating in UK homes well into the 1960s; these homes weren't very warm. A survey made in 1949 and 1950 showed average whole-house temperatures ranging from 12.4 °C to 14.2 °C (Danter, 1951).

With the introduction of North Sea gas in the 1970s also came gas-fired central heating. The proportion of the housing stock with central heating rose from 31% in 1970 to 92% in 2004 (DTI, 2006a). With it also came a presumption that houses should be fully heated to an acceptable comfort temperature. Concerns about death rates, particularly of the very young and the elderly, have given rise to the concept of **fuel poverty**. A household is said to be in fuel poverty if it needs to spend more than 10% of its income on fuel to maintain a satisfactory heating regime (usually 21 °C for the main living area, and 18 °C for other occupied rooms). It has been estimated that in 2004 some 2 million households out of the total of 25 million in the UK were in fuel poverty, and had difficulty in keeping their homes warm at an acceptable cost (DTI, 2006b). Providing adequate levels of insulation is an obvious solution to this.

Yet loft insulation was only introduced into the Building Regulations for new UK houses in 1974 and then only to a depth of 25 mm. Since then standards for new buildings have steadily improved and government campaigns have encouraged householders to install insulation. However, there is still a large proportion of the existing housing stock that is relatively poorly insulated.

The picture for the services sector is not much better. The 1960s saw a fashion for 'curtain wall' office construction where a steel or concrete frame was used to provide the structure and the walls were largely made of thin concrete panels and large sheets of single glazing. These offices were hard to heat in winter and often overheated in summer. Fortunately office buildings tend to be regularly refurbished as new occupants come and go, but even so, making major improvements to the thermal performance can be difficult.

The overall potential for energy savings in both the domestic and services sectors will be discussed at the end of this chapter.

Where references are made to 'the Building Regulations' in this chapter they refer to those for England and Wales. The responsibility for Building Regulations in the UK is devolved to the Regions, i.e. Scotland has slightly different Regulations from those of England and Wales and Northern Ireland. The Regulations for the Republic of Ireland tend to follow a similar pattern to those in the UK.

Space heating energy use

This has been discussed under the topic of passive solar heating in Chapter 2 of Book 2. There it was pointed out that the internal spaces of a building are warmed by heat from:

- the heating system
- 'free heat' gains – from occupants, lights and appliances and from hot water use
- passive solar gains from solar energy penetrating the windows.

It also described the importance of minimising the heat losses in order to achieve a low overall space heating demand. Figure 1.4 shows some of the ways in which heat flows into and out of a house. There are *fabric heat losses*, i.e. those through the building fabric itself; the walls, roof, floor and windows, and *ventilation losses* due to air moving through the building. The heating system may not be 100% efficient, so there may also be flue heat losses. Where hot water is used, there will be another heat loss where

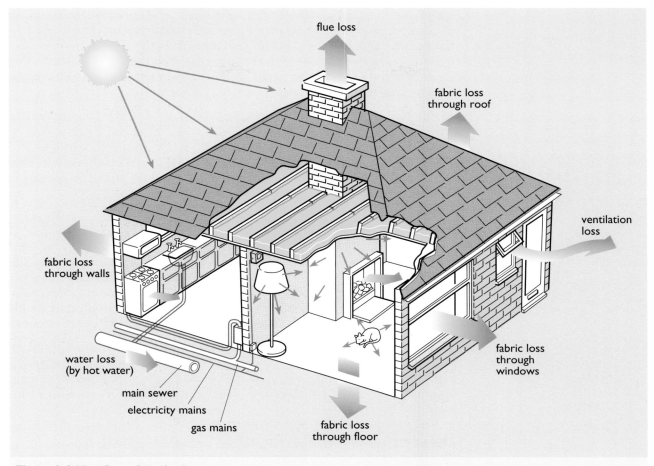

Figure 1.4 Heat flows through a house

this flows away to the sewer. Although this diagram shows a small house, the basic principles also apply to larger buildings.

There are three ways of reducing the space heating energy use:

  (i) cutting the fabric heat losses by the use of insulation

 (ii) cutting the ventilation loss by making the building more airtight and possibly using ventilation heat recovery

(iii) installing a more efficient heating system.

1.2.1 Cutting building fabric heat losses

Insulated windows

Windows can be seen both as pieces of building fabric that need to be properly insulated and as solar collectors gathering passive solar heat gains. They were the main topic of Section 2.4, *The Magic of Glass* in Chapter 2 of Book 2, where the concept of a *U*-value was introduced. As a reminder, it is defined so that:

heat flow through one square metre
= *U*-value × temperature difference

It also described the basic mechanisms that are involved in the transmission of heat: conduction, convection and radiation. They were treated in the context of heat flow through a double-glazed window, stressing the importance of low-emissivity coatings on the glass to reduce radiation loss across the gap between the panes, and of using a heavy gas such as argon to reduce the convection loss.

At the time that Book 2 was written (2003) most of the low-emissivity coatings used in double glazing in the UK were 'hard coat'; a thin layer of tin oxide, giving an emissivity of about 0.15. An improved emissivity of about 0.05 is now commercially available using a 'soft coat' process. This involves depositing onto the glass very thin layers of optically transparent silver sandwiched between layers of metal oxide.

Double glazing was only made mandatory for new houses in England and Wales in 2002. This also had to have a maximum U-value of 2.0 W m^{-2} K^{-1} for windows with wood or PVC-U frames, or 2.2 W m^{-2} K^{-1} for aluminium or steel frames. These values can only be achieved by the use of low-e coatings. They represent a considerable improvement on the U-values of 4.8 W m^{-2} K^{-1} and 5.7 W m^{-2} K^{-1} respectively for their single-glazed counterparts. In 2005 this requirement was extended to all replacement windows for existing houses.

There has also been considerable interest in how these values could be improved on by moving from hard coat to soft coat low-e glass or by adopting triple glazing. Table 1.2 gives some indicative U-values for different glazing options. Even better U-values are possible using krypton gas filling and insulated frames.

Table 1.2 Indicative U-values for windows with wood or PVC-U frames

Glazing type	W m^{-2} K^{-1}
Single glazing	4.8
Double glazing (normal glass, air filled)	2.7
Double glazing (hard coat low-e, emissivity = 0.15, air filled)	2.0
Double glazing (hard coat low-e, emissivity = 0.2, argon filled)	2.0
Double glazing (soft coat low-e, emissivity = 0.05, argon filled)	1.7
Triple glazing (soft coat low-e, emissivity = 0.05, argon filled)	1.3

Source: BRE, 2005

It has been estimated that in 2004, 43% of UK households had some form of double glazing on 80% or more of their windows (BRE, 2006). That, of course, means that there is still a potential for improvement for the other 57% of households.

Insulated walls, roofs and floors

The heat flow through walls, roofs and floors can be reduced by incorporating insulating materials. In order to understand the relative properties of these and the thicknesses required to achieve a given thermal performance for a building, it is necessary to look in detail at heat flow through materials.

Temperatures can be measured in degrees Celsius (°C) or kelvins (K), the only difference being that 0 °C = 273 K. The 'size' of a degree is the same on both scales, so *temperature differences* are identical in °C and K. Current Building Regulations use the kelvin (K) in specifying *U*-values and other thermal quantities, and it is used in this book. In practice *U*-values are widely quoted as W m^{-2} °C^{-1} in architectural literature and the trade press simply because the degree Celsius is more familiar, which is why it was used in Book 2. The actual values are identical in the two cases.

Technical literature can use a range of different presentations of the units of *U*-values: W m^{-2} K^{-1}, W / m^2 K, W m^{-2} °C^{-1} and W / m^2 °C. These are all identical.

Heat energy will flow through any substance where the temperature on the two sides is different, and the rate of this energy flow depends on:

- the temperature difference, $T_{in} - T_{out}$, between the two sides (often written as ΔT)
- the total area available for the flow
- the insulating qualities of the material – its thickness and its **thermal conductivity**.

The thermal conductivity, k, is usually expressed in terms of the rate of heat flow in watts that would flow across a one metre cube of the material with a temperature difference of one degree (kelvin or Celsius) across it (see Figure 1.5):

$$k = \frac{\text{heat flow per square metre of area}}{\text{temperature difference per metre of thickness}}$$

Its unit is therefore W m^{-1} K^{-1} (watts per square metre (W m^{-2}) divided by kelvins per metre (K m^{-1})).

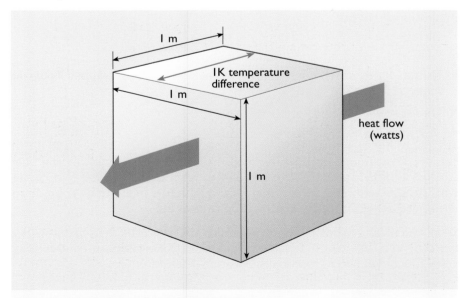

Figure 1.5 Heat flow and thermal conductivity

Table 1.3 below gives thermal conductivities for some common building materials, together with their densities; generally the higher the density, the higher the thermal conductivity.

Table 1.3 Thermal conductivities of common building materials

Material	Density /kg m^{-3}	Thermal conductivity /W m^{-1} K^{-1}
Aluminium (window frames)	2727	220
Stainless steel (wall ties)	7900	17
Reinforced concrete (2% steel)	2400	2.5
Brickwork (outer leaf)	1700	0.77
Plaster (dense)	1300	0.57
Lightweight aggregate concrete block	1400	0.57
Aerated concrete block	600	0.18
Aerated concrete block	460	0.11
Timber (softwood)	500	0.13

Source: Building Regulations Part L2, ODPM, 2001 and manufacturer's literature

Metals have very high thermal conductivities and can transmit large amounts of heat for small temperature differences. Structural building materials such as brick and concrete have lower conductivities but the potential heat losses are still considerable.

Insulation materials (Figure 1.6) make use of the fact that still air, or other gases with a reasonably large molecular weight, are good thermal insulators. Most practical forms of insulation rely on using very small pockets of these gases. There are basically four kinds of commercial insulation material:

■ various grades of aerated concrete containing small bubbles of air
■ foamed glass containing small bubbles of air
■ various forms of wool made up of fibres with air held trapped between them
■ plastic foams containing small bubbles of gas.

Aerated concrete, whose thermal properties are listed in Table 1.2, is obviously not as strong as its dense counterpart. There is a trade-off of compressive strength against thermal insulation performance. In practical construction this material can be used to form the inner leaf of a cavity wall supplementing the main insulation, which is likely to be some form of mineral wool or plastic foam within the cavity.

Wool and plastic foam insulation materials are very light; their densities are typically only 15–30 kg m^{-3}. Table 1.4 below gives some sample conductivity values for them taken from manufacturers' literature.

Figure 1.6 Sample insulation materials (left to right: fibreglass, cellulose fibre, dense rock wool, expanded polystyrene, extruded polystyrene and polyisocyanurate foam)

Table 1.4 Sample thermal conductivity values for insulation materials

Insulation material	Thermal conductivity /W m^{-1} K^{-1}
Foamed glass	0.045–0.055
Sheep's wool, cellulose fibre, mineral wool, glass fibre wool	0.032–0.040
Expanded and extruded polystyrene foam	0.030–0.040
Polyurethane foam	0.025
Polyisocyanurate foam	0.023
Phenolic foam	0.022

Sheep's wool has, of course, been used in clothes as an insulating material for humans for thousands of years. Only now is it considered cheap enough to be used for loft insulation for buildings.

Cellulose fibre insulation is made from shredded recycled newspaper treated with a mineral fire retardant. It can be blown into wall cavities or loft spaces with a special machine.

The most commonly available forms of insulation material are rock wool and glass fibre wool. The naturally occurring rock fibre asbestos is now largely banned because of its associated health problems.

Modern manufactured rock wool is the result of discoveries made in Hawaii of the effects of superheated steam on molten rock during volcanic eruptions. In the manufacturing process a suitable rock is melted at over 1500 °C. It is then spun out through small holes on the perimeter of a centrifuge to produce long, thin fibres. Glass fibre manufacture is similar but using glass. The fibres are then coated in plastic resin and formed into insulation batts.

Plastic foam insulation materials are made by blowing a gas into molten plastic. Expanded polystyrene is a very familiar example widely used for packaging. Other plastics used include urea formaldehyde, polyurethane, polyisocyanurate and phenolic resin. Their foams have different properties. Polystyrene foam, for example, can be made extremely strong and rigid. It can be used under factory floors and is sufficiently strong to carry the

Figure 1.7 A polystyrene house. Despite its solid appearance, this house – built in Milton Keynes in 1986 – used a basic framework of insulating polystyrene blockwork into which concrete was poured. A brick skin was then added on the outside and the inside was plastered

weight of vehicles. It can also be produced in blocks that can be quickly clipped together to build insulating shuttering into which concrete can be poured (see Figure 1.7).

The best thermal insulation performance is achieved by polyurethane, polyisocyanurate and phenolic foams which can have two-thirds of the conductivity of wool materials.

There is considerable debate on the relative environmental friendliness of different materials. Rock wool and fibreglass wool obviously need the use of high temperatures in their manufacture. Plastic foams use oil-based chemicals and, being plastic, are inflammable and can produce toxic smoke when burning. Until the 1990s chlorofluorocarbons (CFCs) were used for blowing these foams. As a result of concerns about environmental effects these have been replaced with other gases with a lower ozone depletion potential: hydrochlorofluorocarbons (HCFCs), carbon dioxide and more recently pentane. The use of the latter, though, increases the potential flammability and suitable precautions have to be taken with its use.

The environmental impact of insulation materials can be reduced through recycling. Recycled materials can be used in glass fibre and some plastic foams, and recycled newspaper is the main ingredient of cellulose fibre insulation. Typically, in a roof insulation application, the energy used in insulation manufacture will be saved within a year.

The most familiar use of wool-type insulation is in loft insulation. Since its first introduction into the UK Building Regulations for housing, the recommended thicknesses have increased from 25 mm in 1974 to 250 mm at present (2006) for both new-build and for existing houses. Figure 1.8 shows the U-values resulting from different thicknesses.

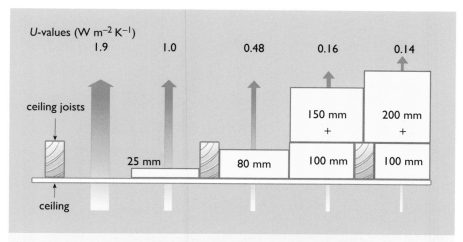

Figure 1.8 Loft insulation thicknesses and U-values (source EST, 2002)

The walls of buildings can be insulated in many ways. In existing buildings with cavity walls foam insulation can be injected into the gap between the two brick skins, or rock wool or polystyrene beads can be blown into it. Typically this will improve the U-value from about 1.5 W m^{-2} K^{-1} to about 0.6 W m^{-2} K^{-1}. This can only be done if the building is not exposed to driving rain, since the main function of the cavity is to stop damp penetration through the wall.

Existing buildings with solid walls can be 'dry lined'. This involves putting a layer of insulation on the inside, faced with plasterboard. This is fairly simple to do. The U-values that can be achieved are mainly dependent on how much reduction in the interior room sizes can be tolerated. For example using 100 mm of rock wool will improve the U-value from 2.1 W m^{-2} K^{-1} to better than 0.45 W m^{-2} K^{-1}.

Alternatively they can be externally insulated, usually with a thick layer of plastic foam which is then either covered with a layer of cement render or a special cladding layer. This is commonly being done in the refurbishment of tower blocks of flats. Although this is relatively expensive, it is possible to achieve good U-values of better than 0.3 W m^{-2} K^{-1} with 100 mm of foam insulation and better than 0.2 with 150 mm.

In new construction, insulation batts can be incorporated into the cavities of brick walls with aerated concrete blockwork used to build the inner leaf (see Figure 1.9). A wall U-value of 0.35 W m^{-2} K^{-1} is currently suggested by the UK Building Regulations. In practice, this can easily be bettered. The cavity can be made as wide as necessary (150 mm to 300 mm) to incorporate more insulation and, if necessary, to retain an air gap to prevent damp penetrating the wall. Timber frame construction can also use considerable thicknesses of insulation as necessary; 200 mm or more of wall insulation is commonly used in Scandinavia and Germany.

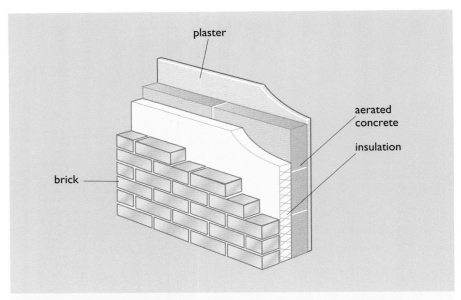

Figure 1.9 Insulation inserted into the cavity of a new wall (Source EST, 2005)

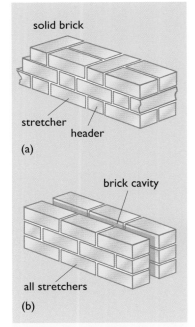

Figure 1.10 Solid and cavity walls

BOX 1.2 **How to tell a cavity wall from a solid brick wall**

Cavity walls can potentially be filled with insulation. All brick walls may at first sight look the same, but on closer inspection the outer skin of a cavity wall, as shown in Figure 1.10, will be seen to be made up of bricks all laid side on (stretchers). A solid brick wall will also include bricks laid end on at right angles (headers).

The floors of buildings can also be well insulated. Modern UK construction often uses aerated concrete or thick sheets of polystyrene or polyurethane foam. In older buildings with suspended timber floors sheets of insulation material can be inserted under the floorboards between the joists. The UK Building Regulations currently suggest a floor U-value of 0.25 W m^{-2} K^{-1} for new buildings and for refurbishment projects.

BOX 1.3 **Calculating U-values of multiple layers of materials**

Thermal conductivities are useful for comparing the thermal properties of different materials (Tables 1.3 and 1.4), but to calculate the properties of a building element consisting of multiple layers of materials we need to use the **thermal resistance** of each layer, its ability to resist the passage of heat.

Consider a slab of a particular material t metres thick, with temperatures T_{in} and T_{out} on the two sides and a heat flow Q watts through each square metre (see Figure 1.11).

The temperature difference per metre of thickness for this slab is $(T_{in} - T_{out}) / t$, so it follows from the definition of thermal conductivity (k) that the heat flow per square metre is:

$$Q = (T_{in} - T_{out}) \times k / t$$

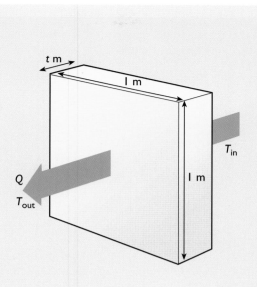

Figure 1.11 Heat flow through a thin slab of material

The *thermal resistance* (R) of the slab is defined as the temperature difference divided by the heat flow per square metre:

$$R = (T_{in} - T_{out}) / Q$$

It follows that $R = t / k$

Since k has units of W m^{-1} K^{-1}, thermal resistance will have units of m^2 K W^{-1}.

Thus for a layer of insulation 100 mm (0.100 m) thick, with a thermal conductivity of 0.04 W m^{-1} K^{-1} the thermal resistance will be:

$$R = \frac{0.1}{0.04} = 2.5 \text{ m}^2 \text{ K W}^{-1}$$

Since the U-value of a slab is the heat flow divided by the temperature difference $R = 1/U$ and $U = 1/R$.

In any practical building element there will be extra thermal resistances, those of the thin layers of air adhering to the outermost and innermost layers of material, and the air in any substantial gap between the layers. Table 1.5 gives standard resistances used for these. Note that the outside surface resistance is much lower than the value used for the inside surface. This is because the air is less likely to be still on the outside and will thus provide relatively less insulation performance.

Table 1.5 Thermal resistances for surfaces and air gaps

Layer	Resistance /m² K W⁻¹
Inside surface	0.13
Air gap	0.18
Outside surface	0.04

The thermal resistances of the components of a building element can be added in series as in Figure 1.12, to give a total thermal resistance (rather like adding electrical resistances in series). The total thermal resistance of a practical building element will thus consist of the sum of those of all its layers plus the inside and outside surface resistances.

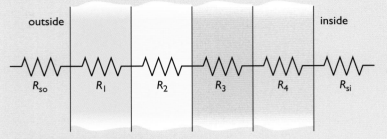

Figure 1.12 Summing thermal resistances

Taking, for example, a wall construction with four layers, the total thermal resistance, R_T , will be:

$$R_T = R_{so} + R_1 + R_2 + R_3 + R_4 + R_{si} \text{ m}^2 \text{ K W}^{-1}$$

The U-value of this wall is its inverse = $1/R_T$ W m^{-2} K^{-1}

For example the wall shown in Figure 1.9 consists of the following layers: 115 mm common brick, a 115 mm cavity filled with mineral wool (conductivity 0.035 W m^{-1} K^{-1}), 115 mm of aerated concrete blockwork (density 460 kg m^{-3}) and a 13 mm layer of plaster on the inside. Using the conductivity values in Tables 1.3 and 1.4 we can calculate its U-value by summing the various thermal resistances as shown in Table 1.6.

Table 1.6 Calculation of thermal resistances

Layer	Thickness /m	Conductivity /W m^{-1} K^{-1}	Resistance /m^2 K W^{-1}
Outside thermal resistance			0.04
Brick	115 mm	0.77	0.115/0.77 = 0.15
Mineral wool	115 mm	0.035	0.115/0.035 = 3.29
Aerated concrete block	115 mm	0.11	0.115/0.11 = 1.05
Dense plaster	13 mm	0.57	0.013/0.57 = 0.02
Inside thermal resistance			0.13
Total thermal resistance			**4.68**

The overall U-value is then:

$$U = 1/R = 1 / 4.68 = 0.21 \text{ W m}^{-2} \text{ K}^{-1}$$

In practice, building elements do not simply consist of flat layers. The wall construction above is likely to use thin metal wall ties securing the outer brickwork to the inner leaf of blockwork. This will create a 'thermal bridge' bypassing the insulation and reducing its performance. A more realistic U-value for this sort of construction is about 0.25 W m^{-2} K^{-1}. Similarly, in Figure 1.8, the loft insulation only blocks the flow of heat over a certain area. There is a parallel heat-flow path through the wood of the joists supporting the ceiling. A certain allowance always has to be made for these thermal bridges, but the mathematics is not simple.

1.2.2 **Cutting ventilation losses**

Buildings also lose heat by **ventilation**, i.e. the passage of air through them. This normally means the controllable air movement through openable windows, extractor fans, or in the case of larger buildings, a mechanical ventilation system. However there is also an uncontrolled component called **infiltration**. This is the air flow through gaps in the fabric of the building; cracks around windows, doors and electrical or plumbing outlets, or between skirting boards and floors.

Some form of ventilation in a building is always essential. For example in a house in winter it is needed in living spaces:

(a) to provide combustion air for boilers, fires and gas cookers, although it is not necessary for heating systems with balanced flues (described later) or for electric fires

(b) to remove moisture from kitchens, toilets and bathrooms, which should be equipped with controllable ventilation openings and/or their own extractor fans

(c) to provide fresh air for occupants and keep them cool in summer.

Ventilation is also needed in other areas of the house, to remove moisture in the roof space or loft above the insulation, or under suspended ground floors (which are usually of wood, but which in more recent construction can be made of concrete). Figure 1.13 illustrates the ventilation and infiltration air paths through a house and also where it is important to maintain essential ventilation.

The main driving forces for this air movement are the buoyancy (or stack) effect of warm air and the wind pressure on a building. Warm air inside a building in winter is less dense than cold air outside and, like a hot air balloon, will tend to rise. This has the effect of sucking in cold air from outside into the rooms on the ground floor. Wind pressure will attempt to force air through gaps in the walls on the windward side of the building and out again on the leeward side. It will be appreciated from Chapter 7 of Book 2 that wind speeds increase with height above the ground, so wind-driven infiltration in high-rise buildings can be a major problem.

Houses are normally **naturally ventilated**, i.e. they are dependent mainly on the stack effect and the wind to provide adequate air movement.

In larger buildings mechanical ventilation is often used. This is often also the means of space heating, with air being centrally preheated (or cooled

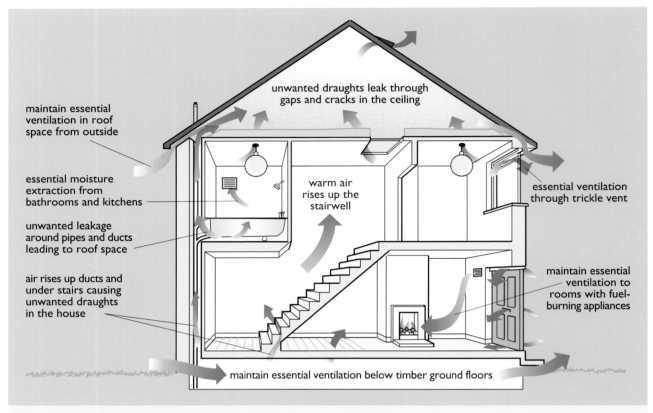

maintain essential
ventilation in roof
space from outside

essential moisture
extraction from
bathrooms and kitchens

unwanted leakage
around pipes and ducts
leading to roof space

air rises up ducts and
under stairs causing
unwanted draughts
in the house

unwanted draughts leak through
gaps and cracks in the ceiling

warm air
rises up the
stairwell

essential ventilation
through trickle vent

maintain essential
ventilation to
rooms with fuel-
burning appliances

maintain essential ventilation below timber ground floors

Figure 1.13 Air leakage paths through a house

in summer) before being distributed throughout the building and extracted again through more ductwork. The term **air conditioning** normally implies the use of mechanical ventilation with central air cooling. The relative merits of natural ventilation and air conditioning are discussed later in this chapter.

The key factor in determining the ventilation heat loss in a building is the **ventilation rate**, i.e. the average rate at which air flows through it. Any air that escapes through the windows, doors and various gaps in the outer fabric is immediately replaced by a new supply of fresh air from outside. We may be unaware of just how substantial this 'invisible' air really is. The average house contains about three-quarters of a tonne of it!

The ventilation rate is normally specified as the number of complete air changes that take place per hour. Actually measuring this scientifically is a fairly complex process. Typically, in a new, really well-built, naturally ventilated house where windows are closed, and with few gaps in the building fabric, it might take two hours for the air to be completely replaced by new, incoming air. We would say that the ventilation rate of this house was 0.5 air changes per hour (written 'ACH').

If the volume of a house is V m³, and the air change rate is n ACH, then the total amount of air passing through it per hour will be $n \times V$ m³. This air needs to be heated up through the temperature difference, ΔT, between the external temperature and the internal temperature. Since the heat capacity per cubic metre of air is 0.33 W m^{-3} K, then the total ventilation heat loss, Q_v, will be:

$$Q_v = 0.33 \times n \times V \times \Delta T \text{ watts}$$

For any given building, the actual ventilation rate will depend on its age and location. Many buildings built before 1919 had an open coal fire and chimney for almost every room. They are also likely to have been designed for gas lighting, with high ceilings and air bricks in the walls to remove the combustion fumes. Draughty wooden ground floors are also common. Since the pressure of the wind on a house has a great influence, buildings in sheltered locations are likely to have a lower air change rate than those in exposed positions. For example, a house built before 1919 might have an average ventilation rate of over 2 ACH in an exposed location.

After 1920 houses and offices were designed for electric lighting and had lower ceilings. It was only in the 1970s, with the advent of cheaper electricity and gas central heating, that houses began to be designed without a provision for open fires. They could then (theoretically at least) be designed to be reasonably airtight.

Airtightness

Proper airtightness is the key to minimising air infiltration. In existing housing this means using draught-stripping, replacing leaky windows and closing off unused chimneys. The latter may be difficult since it is often necessary to maintain a small air-flow through them to remove any moisture penetrating into them. It means paying careful attention to blocking off all the unwanted air leakage paths shown in Figure 1.13, while maintaining the essential ones.

In new construction attention to detail is really important. It is all too easy to leave air gaps around windows and where pipes penetrate walls. Sheet plastic vapour barriers are often built into walls, especially in timber-framed construction. For really good airtightness these vapour barriers must be taped together where they join, so that they cover the whole building envelope. This is quite a skilled job.

The overall airtightness of a building can be assessed with a **pressure test**, as described in the next chapter.

Ventilation heat recovery

Where mechanical ventilation is used, one way of reducing the ventilation heat loss is to use mechanical ventilation with heat recovery (MVHR). This involves allowing the warm outgoing air to preheat the cold incoming air. This can be done by passing both air streams through a **heat exchanger**. As shown in Figure 1.14, this consists of a multiple layer of thin, flat, metal plates with incoming and outgoing air passing through alternate layers. This gives a large area of metal through which heat can flow. Obviously such a system can be used only if the inlet and outlet ducts are adjacent to each other.

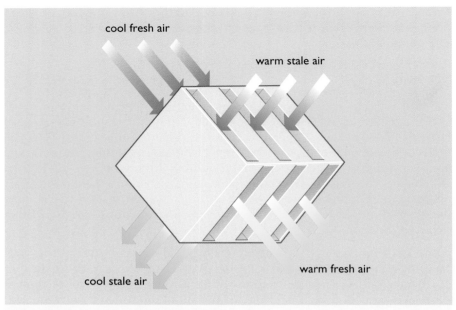

cool fresh air

warm stale air

warm fresh air

cool stale air

Figure 1.14 Flat plate heat exchanger

An alternative approach is to have two quite separate heat exchangers using water as the heat transfer medium, pumped between them in **run-around coils**.

MVHR is a mixed blessing. On the one hand it gives controllable ventilation adjustable to every room. On the other it requires complex ductwork and air pumping which can consume large amounts of electricity. This is a topic that will be revisited later in this chapter.

MVHR systems are available for domestic applications (see Figure 1.15) but it is essential that they are installed in buildings that are really airtight to start with. Otherwise any attempt to pump air around the system may just increase the flow of air through unwanted air infiltration paths. However, once the fabric heat losses of a building have been tackled with thick insulation and high-performance windows, this may be the only satisfactory way to deal with the remaining major heat loss, that from ventilation.

1.2.3 How much insulation does a building need?

The subject of winter temperatures and solar radiation in different parts of Europe has been discussed in the context of active and passive solar heating in Chapter 2 of Book 2. When it comes to determining appropriate levels of insulation, the key factor is the severity of the winter. There are two measures of this: the **winter design temperature** and the **number of degree days**.

The winter design temperature is that of the coldest weather likely to occur on the worst winter days at a particular location. It is used to size the heating system. For example the design temperature for London is −2 °C, while that for Berlin is −11 °C.

The number of degree days is a measure of the average temperature over the winter months and can be used to estimate the heating fuel bills. To work with these it is necessary to calculate the total overall heat loss coefficient of the building in question (see Box 1.4).

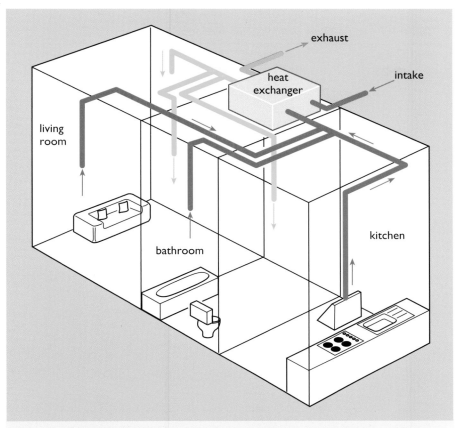

Figure 1.15 Whole-house mechanical ventilation with heat recovery (redrawn from Nicholls, 2002)

BOX 1.4 **Calculating the total heat loss of a house**

If we know the U-values of all the elements of the external fabric of a building, its volume and its average ventilation rate, then we can calculate its overall **heat loss coefficient**. We can define this as the total space heating consumption divided by the temperature difference between the inside and outside air.

Let us take an end-of-terrace house insulated to standards suggested in the 2002 Building Regulations for England and Wales. Its dimensions are shown in Figure 1.16.

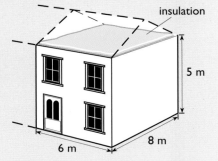

Figure 1.16 An example of an end of terrace house

The total fabric heat loss, Q_f, will be the sum of all the U-values of the individual elements of the external fabric, walls, roof, floor, windows and doors multiplied by their respective areas multiplied by the inside–outside temperature difference, ΔT.

$$Q_f = \Sigma(U_x \times A_x) \times \Delta T$$

The total fabric contribution to the overall heat loss coefficient is then:

$$Q_f / \Delta T = \Sigma(U_x \times A_x)$$

This is calculated in Table 1.7.

Table 1.7 House fabric elements and heat loss

Element	Area /m²	U-value /W m⁻² K⁻¹	Contribution to heat loss coefficient /W K⁻¹
Floor	48	0.25	48 × 0.25 = 12
Roof	48	0.16	48 × 0.16 = 7.7
Walls	80	0.35	80 × 0.35 = 28
Windows and doors	20	2.00	20 × 2.00 = 40
Total			**87.7**

We must also include the ventilation heat loss, which is:

$$Q_v = 0.33 \times n \times V \times \Delta T \text{ watts}$$

where n is the number of air changes per hour (ACH) and V is the volume of the house (m³).

The ventilation contribution to the overall heat loss coefficient is then:

$$\frac{Q_v}{\Delta T} = 0.33 \times n \times V$$

Assuming an air change rate of 0.5 ACH and taking the volume of the house as 240 m³:

$$\frac{Q_v}{\Delta T} = 0.33 \times 0.5 \times 240 = 39.6 \text{ W K}^{-1}$$

Summing the fabric and ventilation contributions gives a total whole-house heat loss coefficient of :

$$\frac{Q_f + Q_v}{\Delta T} = 87.7 + 39.6 = 127.3 \text{ W K}^{-1}$$

Figure 1.17 gives the percentage breakdown of these losses, which shows their relative importance and gives a clue as to where to look for further improvements.

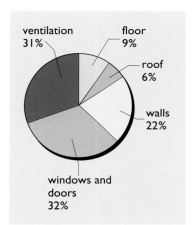

Figure 1.17 Percentage breakdown of heat loss coefficient

We can use this whole house heat loss coefficient to estimate a suitable size for the heating system. If we assume an internal temperature of 20 °C and site the house in London, for example, which has a winter design external temperature of −2 °C, then the heating system must be able to maintain a temperature difference of 22 K. An estimate of the necessary heating system size, Q_h, would thus be:

$$Q_h = 22 \times 127.3 = 2800 \text{ W}$$

If the house was situated in Berlin, which has much colder weather and a design temperature of −11 °C, then the heating system would have to maintain a worst-case temperature difference of 31 °C and would have to be rated at 31× 127.3 = 3950 W.

Obviously the more insulation and the better the airtightness, the smaller (and hopefully cheaper) the heating system can be.

Degree days

We can also use this heat loss coefficient together with the number of degree days to understand how much space heating energy a building might use in different locations. Over a long period, such as a day or so, the heat loss from a building will be proportional to the average temperature difference between the interior and the outside air. If on a given day the average internal temperature was 20 °C and the average external temperature was 10 °C, then the difference would be 10 °C. We would describe that particular day as having '10 degree days'. If on another day the average internal temperature was the same and the external temperature was zero, 0 °C, i.e. an average difference of 20 °C, we would describe that day as having 20 degree days and expect the building to lose twice as much heat as on the first day.

However, if the average external temperature was higher than the interior, then there would not be any heating requirement, and the number of degree days would be zero (rather than a negative number). The total heating requirement over a month will be proportional to the sum of all the degree days of the individual days.

Tables of degree days for different locations for each month of the year are regularly published. Table 1.8 gives some long-term averages for sample UK locations. Given their long history of use, it is not surprising that they are normally produced in the UK with a standard indoor base temperature of 60° Fahrenheit, equivalent to 15.5° Centigrade.

Table 1.8 20-year averages of degree days (to base 15.5 °C) to December 2004 for sample UK areas

	South Western	London (Thames Valley)	Midlands	Northern Ireland	Borders	North-East Scotland
January	281	319	356	343	345	367
February	257	282	314	305	304	327
March	239	242	278	286	295	313
April	193	180	220	227	248	255
May	112	97	136	150	180	183
June	58	44	72	85	106	110
July	25	18	36	46	57	62
August	23	19	37	53	55	66
September	50	48	76	92	95	112
October	111	120	167	174	171	200
November	193	227	264	258	260	285
December	252	293	334	323	327	358
Total	**1794**	**1889**	**2290**	**2342**	**2443**	**2638**

Source: Carbon Trust, 2005

Table 1.8 gives an annual total of 1889 degree days for the London area. A first estimate of an annual heating energy consumption of our house in watt-hours would be the heat loss coefficient, 127.3 W K^{-1}, multiplied by the number of degree days multiplied by 24 (to convert it from days to hours). Dividing by 1000 then gives the result in kilowatt-hours (kWh).

$$\text{Annual consumption} = \frac{127.3 \times 1889 \times 24}{1000} = 5771 \text{ kWh}$$

If the house had been located in Berlin, instead, which has 2600 degree days, then the heating load would have been much higher:

$$\text{Annual consumption} = \frac{127.3 \times 2600 \times 24}{1000} = 7944 \text{ kWh}$$

Put another way, it would have to be better insulated to achieve the same heating demand.

We can go further and say that if we managed to trim 1 W K^{-1} off the heat loss coefficient by better insulation or airtightness, then the marginal saving in space heating demand would be 1889 × 24/1000 = 45.3 kWh in London or 2600 × 24/1000 = 62.4 kWh in Berlin. This could then be used to analyse the relative cost effectiveness of further energy-saving investments.

Balance point temperature

In practice, the degree-day concept should be treated with caution when dealing with well insulated buildings. It may seem strange that degree days are to a base of 15.5 °C and not the actual internal temperature of the building. The degree-day base temperature is assumed to be that below which the heating system is likely to be needed. This is in fact likely to be a function of the degree of insulation. This problem is explored in Figure 1.18 which shows the estimated daily heating requirements for a 1970s house, with and without extra insulation.

On any given day the amount of space heating will depend on the external temperature; the colder it is, the more heating energy will be required. However, there will always be a certain amount of internal free heat gains. The space heating system itself will only need to supply heat if the external temperature falls below a certain 'balance point temperature'. Below this the free heat gains cease to be sufficient to keep the house at the chosen internal temperature, 20 °C in this case. In this particular house in its uninsulated state the balance point appears to be about 13 °C; it is certainly considerably lower than 20 °C. We might say that the heating demand of this house requires degree days to the base 13 °C and not 15.5 °C.

In fact the degree-day concept is very old and predates any notion of insulation in the UK building stock. An assumption of a 'balance point temperature' of 15.5 °C was quite appropriate for estimating the space heating consumption of the buildings of the 1950s and 1960s. As will be described in the next chapter, it is still useful in basic energy monitoring and targeting in existing buildings today.

We can also see from Figure 1.18 that if the house is insulated the balance point falls, to about 9 °C in this example. The free heat gains are now sufficient to keep the house warm in colder weather than before. It is obvious that any accurate estimate of the likely space heating demand needs to

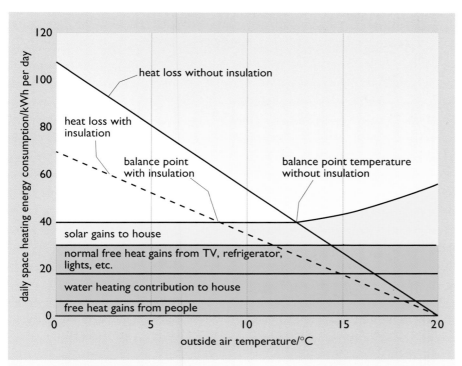

Figure 1.18 Degree days and balance point

take into account not just degree days, but also the shift in balance point temperature with increasing insulation level. The UK Building Regulations for housing are now specified using such a calculation method, the Standard Assessment of Performance (SAP), described further in Chapter 2.

Future insulation standards

The reduction in space heating demand with increasing insulation level has been discussed in Chapter 2 of Book 2. There, a poorly insulated house of the 1970s was described as having a net space heating demand of 13 000 kWh, while a 'well insulated house' i.e. one built to approximately the 2002 Building Regulation standards, achieves a net space heating demand of 4000 kWh, a reduction of 70%.

If a house were sufficiently well insulated – superinsulated – the free heat gains alone should be sufficient to keep the internal spaces warm in all except the coldest weather. A 'space heating system' as such might be very small, or even completely unnecessary. The '3-Liter-Haus' project in Germany (see Box 1.5) has achieved a net space heating demand of 30 kWh yr^{-1} per square metre of floor area (equivalent to 3000 kWh yr^{-1} for a 100 m^2 flat). The German 'Passive House' programme has halved this to a target of 15 kWh yr^{-1} m^{-2} using fabric U-values of approximately 0.1 W m^{-2} K^{-1} (Feist et al., 2005).

The German climate is, as pointed out above, colder than that of most of the UK. Here, the Association for Environment Conscious Building (AECB) has proposed a 'Gold Standard' for new houses with roof U-values of typically 0.1 W m^{-2} K^{-1} and 0.14 W m^{-2} K^{-1} for the walls and floor, together with use of the best triple-glazed windows (AECB, 2005).

BOX 1.5 The 3-litre house

Even the thermal performance of existing buildings can be radically improved if they are adequately insulated. In the late 1990s an estate of apartment blocks in Ludwigshafen (see Figure 1.19) in south-west Germany was given a thorough thermal modernisation including:

At least 200 mm of foam insulation on the roof and in the walls (see Figure 1.20)

Triple-glazed windows with low-e glass with a U-value of 0.8 W m^{-2} K^{-1}

Mechanical ventilation with heat recovery.

Figure 1.20 Laying blocks of foam insulation on a roof on the Brunck Estate (source: LUWOGE picture)

Figure 1.19 The Brunck Estate in Ludwigshafen, Germany (source: LUWOGE picture)

Monitoring showed that the net space heating energy use (i.e. that to be supplied by the heating system) fell by a factor of seven from 210 kWh per square metre of floor area per year to only 30 kWh m^2 yr^{-1}. This is equivalent to 3 litres of heating oil – hence the project name, the '3-Liter-Haus' (Luwoge, 2006).

The project also included a fuel cell combined heat and power (CHP) unit and a phase change wax material in the interior plaster to reduce summer overheating. Work is now completed on a '1-litre' house project.

1.3 Improving heating system efficiency

The rise of central heating

Over the past 50 years the UK has been transformed from a country where the majority of homes were heated with coal fires to one where central heating is almost universal. In 2004, 92% of homes were centrally heated and this proportion is expected to continue to rise.

An open coal fire may seem very cosy and traditional, but in practice most of the heat disappears up the chimney. Its **thermal efficiency**, i.e. the ratio of useful heat output to fuel input, is not very good.

Table 1.9 illustrates the enormous variation in thermal efficiencies of different space heating systems.

Table 1.9 Thermal efficiencies of different space heating systems

Heating system	Seasonal average efficiency
Open coal fire	32%
New coal boiler	70%
Electric fire	100%*
Older gas fire	50%
Typical 1980s wall-hung gas boiler	65%
Gas condensing boiler	>85%

*Ignoring electricity generation and transmission losses

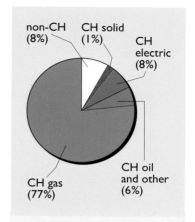

Figure 1.21 UK domestic central heating (CH) fuels, 2004 (BRE, 2006)

In the UK, gas is the dominant central heating fuel (see Figure 1.21) and it also supplies a half of non-centrally heated homes. Renewable energy and energy from waste meet less than 1% of domestic heating energy demand.

This growth of central heating use has been a mixed blessing for overall energy demand. On the one hand it is estimated that the average space heating efficiency has risen from about 50% in 1970 to over 70% in 2004 (BRE, 2006). On the other hand homes are now better heated and estimated average internal temperatures have risen from about 12 °C to 18 °C over the same period, increasing the potential heat losses. It is even possible that this trend will continue to levels of 22 °C or more found in housing in Germany and Scandinavia.

Figure 1.22 shows the layout of a typical domestic **wet central heating system**. Water is circulated through a boiler, which may be fuelled by gas, oil or solid fuel (or even an electric heat pump). The heated water flows through the radiators and also through a heat exchanger in a hot water storage cylinder which holds the **domestic hot water** (DHW) used for washing, etc. The storage cylinder should be well insulated – most are now supplied with a sprayed layer of foam insulation.

There are many variants of this basic system. A common one is the **combination** or '**combi**' boiler. This supplies heat to radiators but dispenses with the hot water cylinder, acting as an instantaneous heater for domestic hot water.

Such a system should obviously be properly controlled for maximum efficiency. A good system is likely to be controlled by:

■ preset time switches, or a timing programmer
■ a room thermostat which senses the air temperature, usually somewhere in the middle of the house
■ a hot water cylinder thermostat which senses the requirement for domestic hot water.

In addition individual radiators should be equipped with **thermostatic radiator valves** (TRVs) which provide extra local control in individual rooms.

Systems for larger buildings are likely to follow a similar pattern, but may have multiple zones which can be separately controlled. Large buildings

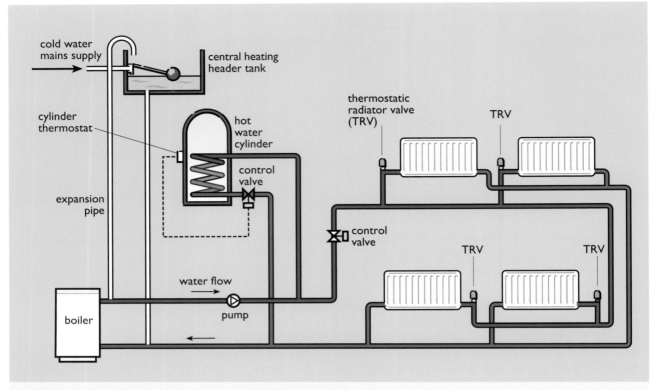

Figure 1.22 A diagram of a radiator, or 'wet', central heating system

such as hospitals are likely to use 'warm air' heating. Air is centrally heated (or cooled) and then blown through ducts to individual rooms. The fan power used and the use of air conditioning has important implications for electricity use and will be discussed later in this chapter.

1.3.1 Gas and oil-fired boilers

Gas boilers

Figure 1.23 shows a simplified diagram of a typical 1980s domestic boiler. Combustion air enters at the bottom from the interior of the house to feed a large gas burner heating a set of finned heat exchangers. Water is pumped through these and circulated out to the heating system. The burnt gases exit at the top into a flue to the outside air. Such a boiler might have an output of 15 kW (or 50 000 British Thermal Units (BTU) per hour – see Box 1.6) and an overall thermal efficiency of 65%.

More recent designs have incorporated a number of improvements:

- **Electronic spark ignition** – these have replaced the permanently burning pilot light used in many older boiler designs which could consume 10% of the total gas used.

- **Balanced flues** – here the burner and heat exchanger are totally sealed off from the interior air of the building and the combustion air is blown through the boiler using an electric fan. Air is drawn in from the outside and the burnt gases are blown out again using a pair of concentric pipes

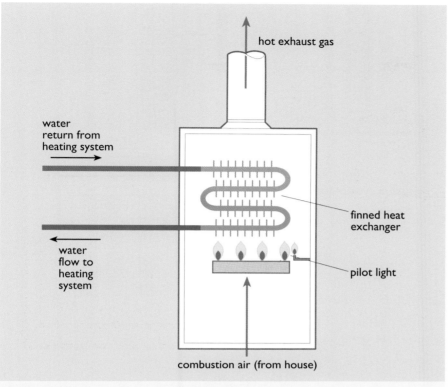

Figure 1.23 Schematic of a typical 1980s gas boiler

BOX 1.6 **BTUs per hour and kilowatts**

Although gas and electricity have been sold in the UK in kilowatt-hours for many years, gas boilers are still sold rated in 'thousands of BTUs per hour'. One BTU (British Thermal Unit) is the amount of heat required to raise one pound of water through one Fahrenheit degree.

1000 BTU per hr = 0.29 kW or 1 kW = 3400 BTU per hr.

---

via a single flue terminal on the outside of the building (Figure 1.24). Although this design does require a certain consumption of electricity, it allows the building to be made more airtight.

■ **Condensing Gas Boilers** – (Figure 1.25) the main component of natural gas is methane, CH_4. When this burns it produces a large amount of water vapour:

$$CH_4 + 2O_2 \rightarrow CO_2 + 2\,H_2O$$

In a non-condensing boiler this vapour is lost with the flue gases. In a condensing boiler the heat exchanger is made sufficiently large so that the return water from the heating system, which may be at about 50 °C, can cool the flue gas to below 100 °C. This enables the water vapour to be condensed out recovering its **latent heat of vaporisation**. This can increase the amount of heat extracted from the gas by 11% (see Box 1.7) and increase the overall boiler efficiency to 90% or more.

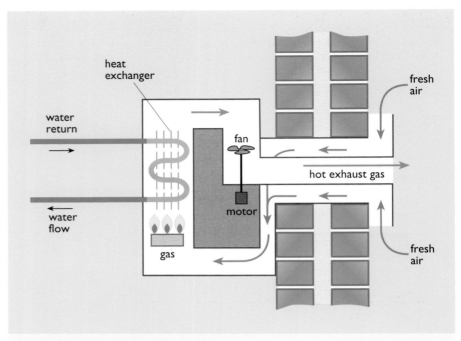

Figure 1.24 Boiler with a balanced flue

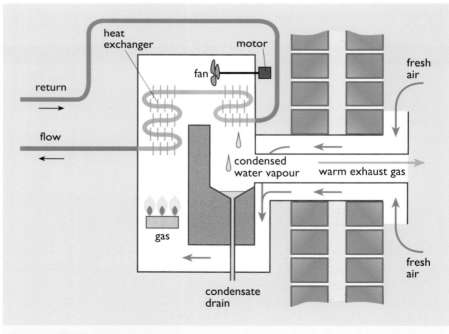

Figure 1.25 Condensing gas boiler

■ **Modular Boilers** – boilers are often very efficient at full load but this can fall off at part load, especially if they have to be turned on and off, or **cycled**, repeatedly. In larger buildings an answer to this is to use a set of small modular boilers rather than one large one. A small heat load can thus be met by running just one boiler at full load.

> ## BOX 1.7 Latent heat and calorific values
>
> The calorific value of a fuel is the heat produced per kilogram when it burns. As combustion produces water in the form of steam (or water vapour), there are always two calorific values:
>
> the higher calorific value (HCV) includes the heat energy released if the vapour condenses
>
> the lower calorific value (LCV) assumes that the water vapour is lost
>
> Table 1.10 gives sample figures.
>
> **Table 1.10** Higher and lower calorific values of fuels
>
> | | Higher calorific value /MJ kg^{-1} | Lower calorific value /MJ kg^{-1} | Ratio |
> |---|---|---|---|
> | Natural gas | 55 | 49 | 1.11 |
> | Heating oil | 45 | 43 | 1.06 |
> | Hydrogen | 142 | 120 | 1.18 |
>
> Source: US DoE, n.d.
>
> Somewhat confusingly the efficiencies of gas boilers are traditionally quoted using the HCV but the efficiencies of engines and power stations use the LCV. For plant fuelled by natural gas this can make an 11% difference. The UK reporting guidelines for quality combined heat and power generation (CHP), which produces both heat and electricity, thus insist that the electrical efficiencies are quoted using the HCV. If you see suspiciously high electrical generation efficiencies always check whether they use LCV or HCV!

Oil-fired boilers

Oil-fired boilers are usually similar in design to gas boilers but need to incorporate a device to vaporise the heating oil before combustion. Condensing boilers are available for use with heating oil, but the potential efficiency improvements are slightly lower, about 6%, because of the lower proportion of hydrogen in the fuel.

SEDBUK and boiler energy ratings

Depending on its age and design a boiler can have an efficiency of anywhere from about 55% to over 90%. This can obviously have a profound effect on the energy consumption of a building and any kind of energy rating. To assist with this the UK Government has compiled a detailed database of boiler types. These have all been individually tested and given a SEDBUK rating (Seasonal Efficiency of a Domestic Boiler in the UK). This database can be viewed online at http://www.boilers.org.uk.

In order to simplify things for purchasers boilers have also been given an Energy Rating Label. Those with a SEDBUK of more than 90% are 'A' rated, those with a SEDBUK figure of 85–90% are 'B' rated, while those with a SEDBUK of below 70% are 'G' rated. From 2005 the UK Building Regulations allowed only A and B rated boilers to be installed.

Although, as pointed out above, average heating efficiencies have improved over the years, there is still a large potential for improvement to a figure of 90% or more.

1.3.2 Electric heating

On-peak electric resistance heating

In the UK electricity has always been considerably more expensive than gas or solid fuel. These relative pricings have been discussed in *Costing Energy*, Chapter 12 of Book 1. Its use for heating has thus been rather restricted. It wasn't until the 1960s that electricity prices had fallen sufficiently against gas and coal that the idea of 'all-electric' homes could be promoted.

Resistance heating using a radiant 'electric fire' or an immersion heater for domestic hot water has been widely promoted as a 'clean' form of heating. Indeed it is very efficient and clean at the point of use, and especially so compared to the dirt and air pollution of coal fires. However, the inefficiency and pollution is effectively transferred to a remote power station. This is reflected in the higher CO_2 emission figures compared to gas heating (see Box 1.8).

While water heating is a year-round activity, space heating is something only required for a part of the year (and possibly only a couple of winter months in a well-insulated building). Thus although an on-peak electric fire is cheap for the consumer to buy, it may be expensive for the industry to supply, requiring power plant that sits idle from spring to autumn.

Off-peak storage heating

The use of off-peak night-time electricity goes some way to reducing the problems of on-peak electric heating use, allowing a daytime load to be shifted to the night. It allowed the demand on the National Grid to be smoothed out and was heavily promoted in the 1960s and 70s. Night-time electricity could be sold at a special low rate that could compete with gas and coal. Domestic hot water could be heated with an immersion heater in a hot water cylinder, but space heating required 'storage heaters'. Figure 1.26 shows a typical design.

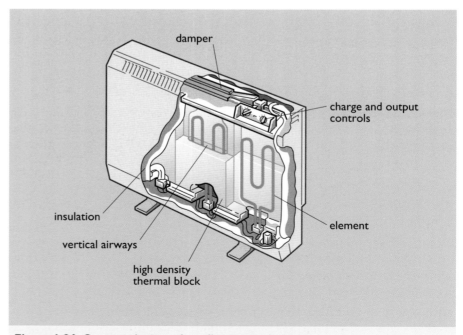

Figure 1.26 Cut-away drawing of an off-peak storage heater

It is basically a set of high-density blocks (similar to bricks) threaded with resistance heating elements inside an insulated casing. The electricity supply is remotely turned on and off by a time switch (usually radio controlled by the National Grid operator). The storage heater itself usually has two manual controls (often poorly understood):

- an 'input' control which sets how much energy needs to be stored overnight according to the weather
- an 'output' control which allows air to circulate through the blocks and into the room.

BOX I.8 Fuels, efficiencies and CO_2 emissions

In assessing any particular building we are likely to be interested in its total fuel consumption and its CO_2 emissions. Section 1.2.1 above has given some guidance on estimating the likely useful heat demand for space heating. Adding an allowance for water heating, the total annual fuel use for heating can thus be calculated as:

$$\text{Total annual fuel use} = \frac{\text{total annual useful heat demand}}{\text{heating system thermal efficiency}}$$

Total annual fuel use = total annual useful heat demand / heating system thermal efficiency

The various heating fuels available all have different CO_2 emission factors, as shown in Table 1.11:

Table I.II CO_2 emission factors for heating fuels

	CO_2 emissions /kg kWh^{-1}
Gas	0.19
Liquefied petroleum gas (LPG)	0.23
Heating oil (gas oil)	0.26
Solid fuel	0.32
Electricity (2004 mix)	0.50

Source: BRE, 2005, 2006

Using these figures we can calculate the total annual CO_2 production:

Annual CO_2 production = Total annual fuel use $\times$ CO_2 emission factor

Consider, for example, a house with a total estimated useful space heating demand of 10 000 kWh yr^{-1} plus a water heating demand of 5000 kWh yr^{-1}. What are its likely annual CO_2 emissions if it is heated: (a) by a condensing gas boiler with a thermal efficiency of 90% or, (b) using off-peak storage heating with an assumed efficiency of 100%?

(a) using a condensing gas boiler:

Total annual fuel use = (10 000 + 5000)/0.90 = 16 667 kWh yr^{-1}

Annual CO_2 emissions = 16 667 $\times$ 0.19 = 3167 kg yr^{-1}

(b) using off-peak electric storage heaters:

Total annual fuel use = (10 000 + 5000)/1.0 = 15 000 kWh yr^{-1}

Annual CO_2 emissions = 15 000 $\times$ 0.5 = 7500 kg yr^{-1}

Thus the electric heating option produces well over twice the CO_2 emissions of the gas option.

The relative lack of control compared to the simple thermostat of a central heating system has long been a source of dissatisfaction with this type of heating. Competition from cheap North Sea gas from the 1970s onwards effectively stopped the spread of electric space heating. Today it is mainly confined to rural areas beyond the gas grid and to urban tower blocks where the use of gas is prohibited for fear of explosions.

Ground Source Heat Pumps (GSHPs)

An alternative to resistance heating is the electric heat pump. GSHPs were introduced in *Geothermal Energy,* Chapter 9 of Book 2. Their basic principle is the same as that of the refrigerator, described in *Electricity*, Chapter 9 of Book 1. Heat is taken from a heat exchanger buried in the ground, raised in temperature using mechanical work delivered by an electric compressor and then delivered to the interior of a building. There it can be distributed via a conventional 'wet' central heating system. The ground source heat exchanger is a set of pipes either in a tube drilled vertically downwards or in a horizontal trench at least 1 m deep.

The **coefficient of performance (COP)** is defined as the ratio of heat delivered to the electrical energy supplied (i.e. unlike that of a refrigerator, where it is the ratio of heat extracted to electrical energy supplied). In a monitored UK GSHP installation the COP averaged nearly 3.2 over the year (EST, 2000).

In practice the COP is dependent on the temperature difference through which the heat pump has to operate; the larger the difference, the worse the performance. This is why ground source heat exchangers are favoured over air source ones (as used for air-conditioning plant). The thermal mass of the ground provides a more stable temperature environment and helps tide the system over really cold weather.

Although heat pumps driven by gas engines have been produced, the GSHP is essentially an electric heating technology. Its attraction is that it reverses the primary energy losses at the power station. If it takes 2.5 kWh of heat to generate 1 kWh of electricity, this can then be turned back into 3 kWh or more of delivered heat energy. Thus in terms of the overall ratio of primary to delivered energy it can be more efficient than using gas boilers.

The CO_2 emissions for GSHPs in the UK are estimated to be only slightly lower than for gas-fired central heating, but considerably better than for oil-fired central heating or electric resistance heating (EST, 2005). At present GSHPs are little used in the UK and are perhaps best suited for buildings beyond the reach of the gas network.

1.3.3 Combined heat and power generation

An alternative to using individual boilers and electric heaters in buildings is combined heat and power generation (CHP). This uses the waste heat from power stations, of many possible sizes. The efficiency benefits of this have been introduced in *Electricity*, Chapter 9 of Book 1. The potential for this is enormous. Figure 1.1 at the beginning of this chapter shows that in 2000 31% of UK primary energy was 'lost in conversion and delivery'. The bulk of this, over 2 EJ, was lost as low-grade waste heat from power stations.

Figure 1.27 A small- scale CHP unit before installation; the engine is at the front and the generator at the rear (courtesy of Cogenco)

This figure should be compared with the 2.4 EJ, shown in the bottom bar of Figure 1.1, used for space and water heating.

As described in Book 1, Denmark in particular has adopted a national policy of widespread use of CHP with **district** or **community heating**, i.e. distributing the heat through large insulated pipes under the streets. In 2000 over half of Danish homes received heat from CHP plants (DEA, 2005).

District heating does not necessarily need to be linked to power stations. It can be supplied from heat-only boilers. It does allow the use of a wide range of fuels, such as energy from waste, biomass, or even solar energy, topics described in Book 2.

In the UK in 2004 there was about 5.5 gigawatts of CHP electricity generation capacity (usually written 5.5 GWe). The bulk of this was large gas or steam turbine plant in industry. In buildings there was about 350 MWe of CHP plant spread over 1100 separate installations. Over 95% of these were spark-ignition gas engines, like the example shown in Figure 1.27.

Such units are essentially heavy-duty lorry engines fuelled by gas and driving a generator. Natural gas is a very clean fuel, so units can be designed to run for 5000 hours a year or more with minimal maintenance, equivalent to a quarter of a million miles for a lorry. Units would normally run as the lead boiler with a set of modular gas boilers providing more heat at times of peak demand. Typically units would range in size from about 50 kWe up to 1 MWe, with electrical efficiencies of 25% up to 40%, large units being more efficient.

Prime users are buildings with large heat and electricity loads such as hospitals and hotels. Leisure centres with swimming pools are particularly appropriate because of the very large low-temperature heat requirements of the pools, which allow CHP units to be run in condensing mode with an almost 90% overall fuel efficiency.

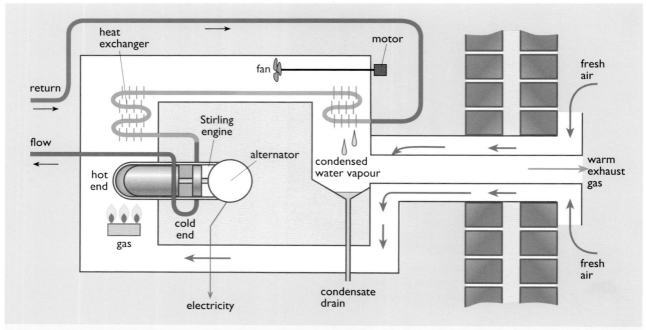

Figure 1.28 Schematic diagram of a single-cylinder domestic micro-CHP unit

This is a technology that has been heavily promoted in the past, but has run into difficulties with the current form of the electricity market, the British Electricity Trading and Transmission Arrangements (BETTA). These require that any electricity exported must be precisely predicted hours in advance. Thus there is a tendency for CHP units currently being installed to be sized only to meet the local building electricity demand without exporting, which fails to take advantage of the economies of scale in using large machines.

Between 1999 and 2004 the amount of installed capacity in buildings only increased by 38 MWe (DTI, 2000, 2005a), which can hardly be regarded as a success story.

Stirling Engine Domestic Micro-CHP

Over the past ten years, small CHP units of approximately 1 kW electrical output have been developed, intended as replacement domestic gas boilers. These use a small Stirling engine to drive a generator (see *Oil and Gas Engines*, Book 1 Chapter 8 for more on Stirling engines). These are packaged as a condensing gas boiler which also generates electricity, as shown in Figure 1.28. The design is basically similar to the boiler shown in Figure 1.25, but additionally, high temperature heat is supplied to the 'hot end' of the Stirling engine, and low temperature waste heat is recovered from the 'cold end'. A similar design using a four-cylinder engine, the Whispergen, is now being marketed.

These units are primarily designed to meet the heat load of a house but not to continuously generate the full electricity demand as well. If the electricity demand for the house is larger than the output of the generator, all the electricity will be used. If the output exceeds the demand, then it will be exported to the grid via a suitable two-way meter.

It is suggested that if large numbers of these were to be installed the total amount of electricity produced at any given time would be a reasonable approximation to the average domestic electricity load. Their installation would thus have a beneficial effect on the grid in reducing both average and peak transmission loads from conventional power stations.

The electrical generation efficiency for these commercial units is not high, a figure of 10–12% being quoted for the four-cylinder Whispergen. However, prototype machines have been built with higher efficiencies.

The potential for this technology is enormous. A report by the Society of British Gas Industries (SBGI, 2003) suggests that these could potentially be retrofitted in 14 million UK homes, with an estimated annual CO_2 emission saving of 1.5 tonnes per year per unit.

Fuel cell CHP

Fuel cells were introduced in Chapter 14 of Book 1 and further described in Box 10.3 of Book 2. CHP units using these are now becoming commercially available and are widely used in the USA and Japan.

In 2001 a 200 kWe phosphoric acid fuel cell (PAFC) was installed at a leisure centre in Woking as part of a scheme incorporating a further 1 MWe of gas engine CHP and 9 kWp of photovoltaics. The hydrogen to run the fuel cell is produced by reforming natural gas. The individual fuel cell elements are stacked together to produce approximately 400 volts DC, and this is coupled to the grid via an AC inverter. Hot water from the fuel cell is used not just to provide heating, but also to run an absorption chiller unit for cooling for the leisure centre. Performance monitoring showed that the fuel cell operated with approximately the same electrical generation efficiency, 37%, as a comparable gas engine CHP unit (DTI, 2005b).

Small prototype domestic fuel cell CHP units are also undergoing trials. The proton exchange membrane fuel cell (PEMFC) may be the most suitable for these because it can be started up in a matter of minutes, whereas other types may best be used continuously. These prototype systems are being produced with an electrical output of 1–1.5 kW, an electrical generation efficiency of over 35% and an overall fuel efficiency of over 80% (SBGI, 2003).

At present both the capital costs and maintenance costs are higher than for gas engines, but these could fall in the future. Fuel cell CHP has two main advantages over engine-driven CHP: the units are almost silent, with no moving parts, and they have high electrical efficiencies which in the longer term could reach 50%, i.e. competitive with large combined cycle gas turbine (CCGT) power stations (IEA, 2005).

Using waste heat from large power stations

This is an option hardly used at all in the UK, since the trend has been to build large coal-fired power stations well away from major built-up areas. However, many gas-fired power stations are close to major urban centres. For example the 1 GWe Barking CCGT station is less than 20 km from central London and pumps hundreds of MWs of waste heat into the Thames.

There is obviously enormous potential for using waste heat from such large power stations, but it comes at a cost of reduced electricity generation efficiency. As described in *Heat to Motive Power,* Chapter 6 of Book 1, most large power stations employ cooling towers or heat exchangers in the sea or rivers. This allows the use of a condenser to reduce the steam temperature at the output of the low-pressure turbine to well below 100 °C. Yet a district heating system needs to be fed with low-pressure steam at typically 110 °C. What are the implications of this?

The example in Chapter 6 of Book 1 considers a coal-fired steam turbine station with a turbine inlet temperature, T_{in}, of 600 °C (873 K) and an outlet temperature, T_{out}, of 45 °C (318 K).

The Carnot efficiency

$$= \frac{(T_{in} - T_{out})}{T_{in}} \times 100 \text{ (where the temperatures are in kelvins)}$$

$$= \frac{(873 - 318)}{873} \times 100 = 63.3\%$$

If we now increase the outlet temperature to 110 °C (383 K), the Carnot efficiency then becomes:

$$= \frac{(873 - 383)}{873} \times 100 = 56.1\%$$

i.e. there has been a 7.2% loss in efficiency in terms of work (and thus electricity) produced in exchange for some low-temperature heat.

Any practical large CHP plant is likely to have varying heat and electrical demand. The trade-off between heat and electricity is known as the Z factor. A Z factor of 6 would mean a loss of one unit of electricity for every 6 units of heat produced. This is typical for low-pressure steam taken from a steam turbine power station. Extracting high-temperature water from a CCGT station, with its higher overall thermal efficiency, has less effect on the overall electrical efficiency. It has been suggested that a Z factor of 10 could be achieved with a purpose-built CCGT CHP station (PB Power, 2005).

Which is best?

There are many possibilities for CHP. Which is best is a matter of location and trade-offs of cost and performance. Generally, the larger the CHP unit, the higher the electricity generation efficiency, the lower the capital costs per kW of capacity and the lower the maintenance costs per kWh of electricity produced.

According to a Building Research Establishment study there is an economic potential for 18.3 GW of CHP in UK domestic, commercial and public buildings. This would allow 5.5 million homes to use CHP, i.e. about a quarter of the housing stock. (BRE, 2003). The study was based on using reciprocating gas engines, but comments that after large areas have been connected there could be economies of scale by switching to using larger CCGT plant.

A recent International Energy Agency report (IEA, 2005) modelled the heating needs of a European city of about 250 000 inhabitants (based on Leicester). It compared different forms of CHP with a base case of using individual condensing gas boilers and electricity from new, high-efficiency CCGT plant. It concluded that the least-cost solution, and the one with the largest CO_2 emission savings, was city-wide CHP using heat and electricity from a CCGT power station. This leaves many buildings in suburban areas for which individual small CHP units may well be the best solution. However, if small fuel cell CHP units can be produced with high efficiencies and low maintenance costs then these could become serious challengers to city-wide CHP.

1.4 Saving electricity

1.4.1 Electrical appliances

Cutting electrical demand in buildings requires tackling a whole range of uses. Chapter 9, *Electricity*, in Book 1 has described how mains electricity started as a lighting technology, but then rapidly diversified into motive power and then a host of electrical appliances. Figure 1.29 shows the recent changes in the ownership of some of these. TV ownership isn't shown, but by 2004 the average UK household owned 2.4 of them (EST, 2006).

Not only is the ownership of appliances per household increasing, so is the number of households. The UK population is likely to increase

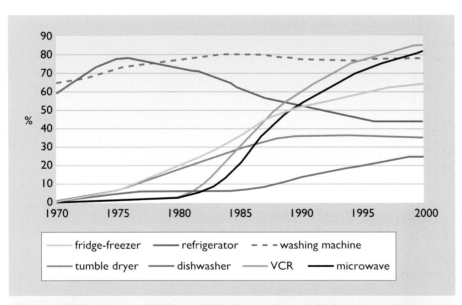

Figure 1.29 Percentage of UK households that own household domestic appliances (Source DTI, 2006a)

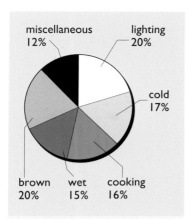

Figure 1.30 UK 2004 domestic electricity use by lights and appliances – total 89 TWh (source DTI, 2006a)

from almost 61 million in 2006 to around 67 million by 2050, but the average household size is also falling. It is currently about 2.5 persons per household, but this is likely to fall to 2.1 persons by 2050. The total number of households could thus rise from about 25 million today to nearly 32 million by 2050 (Boardman et al., 2005). Into every new household goes a new set of appliances.

In 2004 electricity use by domestic appliances and lighting amounted to 89 TWh, about a quarter of total national demand. Figure 1.30 shows the breakdown into different categories: lighting, cooking, 'cold' appliances (i.e. fridges and freezers), 'wet' appliances (washing machines, tumble dryers, dishwashers), 'brown' appliances (TVs, radios and hi-fis) and 'miscellaneous' (a host of gadgets including computers, video games, mobile phone chargers, etc.) Although this shows a snapshot for 2004, the use in these latter two categories has been increasing rapidly and poses a serious problem for programmes to reduce electricity demand.

Standby power

Perhaps the most disturbing wastage of electricity is that from millions of small devices that are not fully switched off but are left on 'standby'. The situation was summarised by a recent House of Lords Select Committee report:

> The effect of standby consumption, at a national level, is breathtaking: in the United Kingdom television sets alone consume some 90 million kWh per month in standby mode. This is approximately equivalent to the continuous output of a small—120 MW—power station. It translates into greenhouse gas emissions approaching 150,000 tC/year. Moreover, these figures apply only to televisions, and fail to take account of all the other forms of equipment—audio equipment, video or DVD players, computers, photocopiers—which revert to standby mode when not in use. The Government estimate that overall no less than 760 million kWh per month of electricity are consumed by appliances not actually in use—the equivalent of 1 GW continuous output, or some 2.25 percent of total United Kingdom electricity consumption, producing of the order of 1.2 MtC per annum.
>
> (House of Lords Science & Technology Committee, 2005)

The problem with devices such as televisions is that they have been designed for 'convenience', with little regard to energy use. To allow the TV to be turned on by a remote control from an armchair, the power supply is left running permanently, just to power a small infrared sensor and a relay. The situation has not improved with the development of digital television. This requires an integrated receiver decoder (IRD) or set-top box (STB) specifically designed to be left on permanently to allow 'off-peak' downloading of TV programmes for 'view on demand'.

Another problem arises with 'mains adapters' and battery chargers. Electronic devices are sold worldwide. In order to simplify compliance with safety regulations about high voltages in appliances, they are often designed to be run from low-voltage supplies. A separate adaptor is then supplied to provide the required voltage (6V or 12V) from the local mains supply, 120 volts AC or 230 volts AC. Thus although the actual electronic device may be switched on and off, the mains adaptor or charger usually remains plugged in and permanently switched on. The situation is compounded by the use of low-quality transformers which still draw current through the primary coil although none is being taken from the low-voltage secondary coil. The result is a continual dissipation of heat.

The solution is better design and enforced international standards, such as the new 2005 European Energy-using Products (EuPs) Directive. The regulation for standby power says quite simply '*As a general principle, the energy consumption of EuPs in stand-by or off-mode should be reduced to the minimum necessary for their proper functioning*' (EU, 2005). A long-term target for a maximum standby power is 1 watt. This Directive should become law in the UK in 2007.

Figure 1.31 A large-screen plasma TV uses far more electricity than a CRT TV

Televisions and consumer electronics

In use, a typical cathode ray tube (CRT) television of today consumes about 100 watts and a large-screen plasma TV (see Figure 1.31) may use 500 watts. These and other electronic devices represent an increasing use of electricity in the home. In the office, the increased use of electronic equipment is a source of excess heat which may promote the installation of air conditioning.

Yet the electronics industry is capable of great feats of energy efficiency if pressed. The laptop computer is carefully designed to eke out the absolute maximum period of operation from the minimum battery capacity. Liquid crystal displays (LCDs) are universally used in them. They can use only 10% of the electricity of an equivalent CRT display. Although LCD displays are likely to compete with plasma screens for the 'widescreen' market, screen sizes and consequence power ratings are likely to increase in the future. A study by the Environmental Change Institute (Boardman et al., 2005) suggests that UK domestic electricity use in consumer electronics could double by 2050 to over 20 TWh yr^{-1}.

Refrigerators

In domestic use a **refrigerator** or **fridge** usually has a main cabinet with a temperature of around +5 °C and may have an icebox (freezer compartment) maintained at −5 °C. A **freezer** has a lower internal temperature of around −18 °C. Combinations, known as **fridge-freezers**, have become increasingly common in recent years.

In 2004 domestic refrigeration in the UK used an estimated 15 TWh of electricity per year, almost 4.5% of total demand (DTI, 2006b). This figure is down from a peak of 17.5 TWh in 1998 due to the improved energy efficiency of new fridges on sale. However these figures have to be compared with the 2 TWh used for refrigeration by the food processing industry. This presumably handles exactly the same food and stores it for longer periods, but it does so in physically larger and more energy-efficient cold stores.

It is worth reflecting on the energy consequences of having a fridge in every home. Back in the 1930s a home would have had only a cold domestic larder and shopping was done almost daily. Frozen food (such as there was) would have been stored in a large-volume grocer's cold store. It is now considered more convenient to shop weekly and have a refrigerator in every home. A result of this 'distributed cold storage' has been to increase the total heat loss area and consequent energy requirements for cooling (see Box 1.9).

BOX 1.9 **The energy consequences of a fridge in every home**

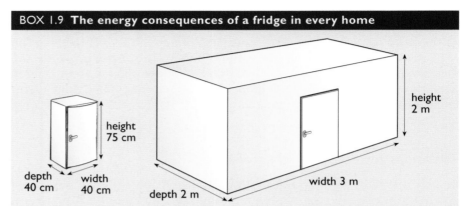

Figure 1.32 Two alternatives for cold storage – a domestic refrigerator and a grocer's cold store

A typical small domestic fridge has an internal temperature of +5 °C and its external dimensions are 40 cm × 40 cm × 75 cm. It is situated in a room with a temperature of 17 °C. Its sides have a U-value of 1.5 W m^{-2} K^{-1}. What is its volume (assuming minimal wall thickness) and its heat loss in watts?

How does this compare with a grocer's cold store whose dimensions are 2 m × 2 m × 3 m with the same internal and external temperatures and U-value?

First, taking the domestic refrigerator:

$$\text{Volume} = 40 \times 40 \times 75 \; = \; 120\,000 \text{ cm}^3 \; = \; 120 \text{ litres}$$

$$\text{Surface area} = 2 \times \big((40 \times 40) + (40 \times 75) + (40 \times 75)\big) \text{cm}^2$$

$$= 2 \times (1600 + 3000 + 3000) \text{cm}^2 = 15\,200 \text{ cm}^2$$

$$= 1.52 \text{ m}^2$$

Temperature difference between inside and outside = $17 - 5 \; = \; 12$ K

Heat loss = U-value × area × temperature difference

$$= 1.5 \text{ W m}^{-2} \text{ K}^{-1} \times 1.52 \text{ m}^2 \times 12 \text{ K} = 27.4 \text{ watts}$$

Heat loss per litre of storage space $= \dfrac{27.4}{120} = 0.23$ watts litre^{-1}

For the cold store:

$$\text{Volume} = 2 \times 2 \times 3 \; = \; 12 \text{ m}^3$$

$$= \; 12\,000 \text{ litres (i.e. 100 times as large as the refrigerator)}$$

$$\text{Surface area} = 2 \times \big((2 \times 2) + (2 \times 3) + (2 \times 3)\big) \text{m}^2$$

$$= 32 \text{ m}^2$$

Heat loss = $1.5 \; \times 32 \times 12 = 576$ watts

Heat loss per litre $= \dfrac{576}{12\,000} = 0.05$ watts litre^{-1}

It is obviously more energy efficient (by a factor of almost 5!) to have a few large cold stores rather than large numbers of small refrigerators. The mathematical reason for this is that the storage volume increases as the cube of the dimensions while the surface area only increases as the square of them. In practice, this energy ratio might be even larger if the thickness of the grocer's cold store was increased in line with the overall dimensions. If the wall U-value was improved to 0.3 W m^{-2} K^{-1} then its heat loss would be only 115.2 watts, equivalent to just over four domestic fridges.

Until the 1980s there was little interest in the UK in producing 'energy efficient' fridges. It paid designers to maximise the internal storage space even if that meant cutting down on insulation thickness. Electricity bills were a secondary consideration. Yet the potential for saving was enormous. The average consumption for a European 200 litre larder fridge (i.e. one without a freezer compartment) in 1973 was 550 kWh yr^{-1}. A Danish unit produced in 1988 showed that electricity consumption could be drastically cut. Better insulation reduced the heat loss and an improved COP was achieved by fitting a larger evaporator and condenser (Nørgård, 1989). A similar fridge is now sold with a quoted electricity consumption of 160 kWh yr^{-1} and an 'A' rating under the current European Energy Labelling scheme (see Chapter 2).

Most fridges use electric heat pumps (as described in Book 1), but refrigeration can also be achieved using **absorption cycles**. Domestic gas-powered fridges were widely available in the 1960s and there is continued interest in absorption cycle refrigeration for use in air conditioning. The efficiency of fridge motors can also be improved by lowering the running voltage after starting (see Section 1.4.3 for more on both these topics).

Current (2006) 'A' rated fridge designs use about 25 mm of insulation thickness, while freezers use about 50 mm. Improved efficiency can always be achieved with thicker insulation. However, the external dimensions are fixed in practice by the standard units of width and height of fitted kitchens, so improved efficiency will usually mean less internal storage space. Yet adding an extra 25 mm of insulation to the interior of the fridge in Figure 1.32 would only reduce its interior volume by 3%. The way forward may be through the use of better insulation, such as vacuum insulation panels (see Box 1.10). If this can be developed and the manufacturers' reluctance to trade storage volume for insulation thickness can be overcome, then the fridges of 2050 could each use under 100 kWh yr^{-1}. UK domestic total electricity use by 'cold' appliances could have fallen by a factor of five from its peak 1998 level to only 3.5 TWh yr^{-1}. (Boardman et al., 2005).

BOX 1.10 Vacuum Insulated Panels (VIP)

The idea of vacuum insulation has been around for a long time. Sir James Dewar, a scientist at Oxford University, invented a 'vacuum flask' in 1892, as a container for low temperature liquefied gases. This consisted of two glass flasks one inside the other with a vacuum in between ensuring that no heat could flow by conduction across the gap. The glass surfaces were also given a low-emissivity coating of silver to prevent heat radiating across it.

This was turned into a commercial product, the 'Thermos flask', in 1904 by two German glassblowers. It has been the standard receptacle for carrying hot drinks to picnics ever since. Large Thermos flasks of up to 125 litres capacity were developed for cold food storage in the late 1920s, but these were overtaken by the rise of the modern refrigerator.

The development of flat 'vacuum panel' insulation is fraught with many difficulties. The most basic is that of resisting the pressure of the air. A panel one square metre in size would have to resist a force equivalent to about 10 tonnes.

One approach is to take a plastic foam or an 'aerogel' made from silica, wrap it in a thick airtight plastic cover and pump any air or gases out. As long as the foam has sufficient strength not to collapse under the atmospheric pressure, thermal conductivities of under 0.005 W m^{-1} K^{-1} can be achieved at pressures of around 1 mbar. This represents a fourfold improvement over the best non-evacuated plastic foam insulation. There are still many problems to be solved to maintain this performance over a long period of time since any pinholes in the outer layer could destroy the vacuum. Although VIPs are now commercially available, they are expensive and there are likely to be trade-offs of production cost against life expectancy.

Adapted from Glacier Bay, n.d.

Washing machines and 'wet appliances'

As shown in Figure 1.30, washing machines and heated dryers, together with dishwashers, account for some 15% of UK domestic electricity consumption and few dramatic improvements seem to be expected. The use of high-speed spin dryers in washing machines reduces the need for heat energy in tumble dryers. Most washers already have an 'economy cycle', which uses lower temperatures and less heated water but more agitation over a longer period.

Similarly, energy-efficiency improvement in dishwashers has concentrated on using less water, since heating the water is where most of the energy is used. Although ownership is expected to increase, UK domestic energy use in wet appliances may only reduce by 20% by 2050 (Boardman et al., 2005).

Cooking

Energy use in domestic cooking has been steadily declining since the 1970s, in part due to the increased use of microwave ovens and pre-prepared meals. This raises the question of the total energy used in producing these. A recent report (AEA Technology, 2005) estimated that the total energy input for a 'chicken ready meal' to the dinner plate was 9.7 kWh kg^{-1}, including only about 1 kWh for the final reheating. The alternative of buying and cooking a whole chicken would have a higher overall energy input, 13.2 kWh kg^{-1}, of which over 6 kWh would be the final cooking in the home.

As with wet appliances, few breakthroughs in cooking technology seem likely in the foreseeable future.

1.4.2 Energy-efficient lighting

In 2004 lighting in buildings accounted for about 15% of UK electricity use. The domestic sector used approximately 18 TWh and the services sector a further 37 TWh, of which over a third was used in retail premises.

Chapter 9 of Book 1 has described the development of the different types of lamp and introduced the concept of **luminous efficacy**, the amount of light emitted in **lumens** by a lamp per watt (lm W^{-1}) of electricity used. Box 1.11 shows the types of lamps currently available and Figure 1.33 shows how, for

BOX 1.11 Lamp types and their efficacies

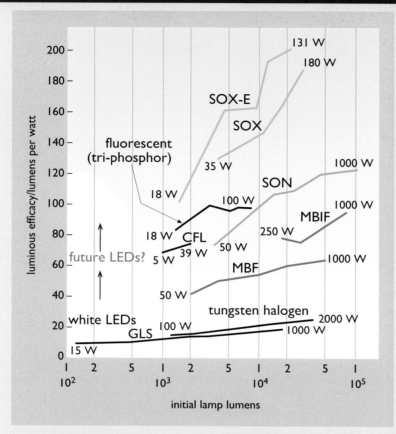

Figure 1.33 The efficacies of various lamps (adapted from Beggs, 2002)

Table 1.12 Descriptions of lamp types

Lamp type	Details
General lighting service (GLS)	The common incandescent light bulb
Tungsten halogen	Miniature incandescent lamps, often run on a 12-volt supply from a transformer
Fluorescent high-pressure mercury discharge lamp (MBF)	Bluish white light, often used for shop lighting
Metal halide high-pressure mercury discharge lamp (MBIF)	Bluish white light, used for street lighting
Compact fluorescent lamp (CFL)	Replacement for normal incandescent light bulbs
Tri-phosphor tubular fluorescent	Standard type for office and shop lighting
High-pressure sodium discharge lamp (SON)	Orange-white light, used for street lighting
Low-pressure sodium discharge lamp (SOX) and higher-efficacy version (SOX-E)	Pure orange light, used for street lighting
Light-emitting diode (LED)	Available in a range of colours and bluish white

a given type, lamp efficacy increases with wattage. Very high efficacies are available for street lighting, but most of the applications in buildings require lamps of under about 3000 lumens output. Despite the availability of compact fluorescent lamps, standard low-wattage (and low-efficacy) incandescent lamps and small tungsten halogen lamps remain widely sold.

Light-emitting diodes (LEDs) are relative newcomers to the list. Although familiar as small indicator lights, they have now been developed in a range of colours, and more recently in a bluish white. This has been produced using a blue LED but adding a phosphor, using the 'rare earths' cerium and yttrium, which converts some of the blue light to a broad yellow spectrum.

One attraction of LEDs is their potentially long life, tens of thousands of hours, compared to 1000–2000 hours for an incandescent lamp or 8000 hours for a compact fluorescent lamp. Although they are currently mass-produced as small lights of under 1 watt output, these can be built up into modules that can compete with small incandescent lamps. At present efficacies in commercial lamps are around 25 lm W^{-1}, but a performance of over 100 lm W^{-1} has been demonstrated.

In the longer term these have the potential to produce dramatic cuts in domestic lighting consumption. It has been suggested that by 2050 this could have fallen by a factor of four from current levels to around 4 TWh yr^{-1} (Boardman et al., 2005).

Efficient lighting isn't just about using high-efficacy lamps. It is also about properly illuminating the things that we want to see, such as reading this book.

A typical incandescent light bulb emits light in all directions. We talk of this 'flow' of light as the **luminous flux** emitted by the lamp. When a lamp is mounted in a 'light fitting' or **luminaire**, the flow of luminous flux will be concentrated in one particular direction (e.g. downwards in the case of a normal ceiling luminaire). A certain number of lumens are therefore concentrated in a particular direction.

When we come to the practical aspects of 'seeing what we are doing' we need to know about the amount of light falling on a given surface. This is known as the **illuminance** and has the SI unit, the **lux**. One lux is defined as a luminous flux of 1 lumen falling on an area of 1 m^2.

For example, the diners (*circa* 1910) in Figure 1.34 may be enjoying their electric light. They are also being energy efficient. Hanging the bulb close over the table may have been necessary, not just because of the low efficacy of incandescent lamps, but also because they were paying, in real terms, at least four times today's price for electricity.

Are they likely to be getting an adequate illuminance on their table? The energy radiated by the lamp spreads out over a larger area as the distance from the lamp increases (Figure 1.35). Suppose that the table, with an area A square metres, receives the full beam when the lamp is at a distance d from it. If the lamp was at a distance $2d$, the beam would spread over *four* times the original area. At this distance the table would only receive a quarter of the full beam. In other words, *doubling* the distance has reduced the illuminance

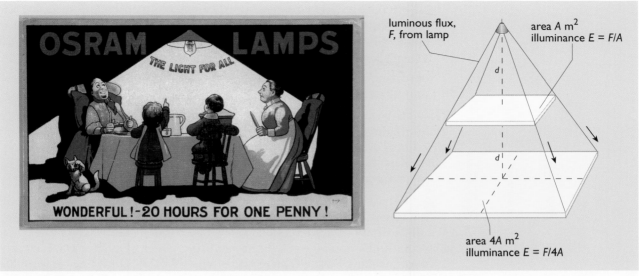

Figure 1.34 An early advertisement for (rather expensive) electric lighting (courtesy of Mary Evans Picture Library)

Figure 1.35 The inverse square law of illumination

by a factor of four. This **inverse square law** applies to any simple light source (except where the beam is focused by lenses or mirrors).

If we assume in Figure 1.34 that the lamp is rated at 40 watts and has an efficacy of 5 lm W^{-1} (a typical figure for 1910), then it will be producing 200 lumens. The luminaire (the lampshade) may only be 75% efficient, so a total of only 150 lumens will be projected downwards. If we assume that a half of this, 75 lumens, actually shines on the table, and that this has an area of 1 m^2, then the illuminance is 75 lm m^{-2} or lux.

Artificial lighting schemes are usually specified as being capable of supplying a specified number of lux on a horizontal surface – the 'working plane'. Generally the more demanding the work, the higher the required level of illuminance. Table 1.13 gives some recommended values.

Table 1.13 Recommended illuminance levels

Task	Recommended illuminance /lux
Circulation areas (stairs, corridors)	150
Classroom desk	300
Office desk, laboratory bench	500
Electronics assembly	1000
Hospital operating theatre	2000

The danger of a list like this is that it can be taken as a specification for a whole building. Large open-plan offices can be designed so that an illuminance of 500 lux is provided everywhere. This allows the occupants the freedom to position desks wherever is most convenient. A more energy-efficient approach would be to employ:

- task lighting – individual controllable lighting for each workplace with a lower level of background illuminance
- occupancy sensors, for example in corridors to turn on lights only when they are needed.

It also pays to maximise the efficiency of the lighting by good maintenance of luminaires. Fluorescent lamps are often seen dimly through dirty and discoloured plastic diffusers with a stock of dead flies. Modern, high-efficiency, reflective luminaires can be over 80% efficient in reflecting light downwards.

Also, the best use should be made of daylight. Sunlight is extremely bright and its illuminance can reach 100 000 lux on the ground. However as a light source it suffers from rapid fluctuations caused by passing clouds. Under overcast sky conditions normal daylight has an illuminance of at least 5000 lux and is more constant. Daylight penetrating windows into a building can provide illuminance levels of around 200–300 lux in typical naturally lit offices for most of the working day. The difficulty is in persuading occupants to turn off the artificial lights. This is part of a more general problem of behavioural attitudes to energy efficiency that will be discussed in Chapter 3.

1.4.3 Ventilation and air conditioning

This is a slightly controversial subject. Traditionally, UK buildings have been naturally ventilated. However, as described in Section 1.2.1, cutting winter ventilation heat loss may require the construction of airtight buildings and the use of mechanical ventilation with heat recovery. This in turn will require the use of electricity to pump air around the building.

Also, UK buildings have not traditionally required cooling. However, climate change brings with it the possibility of higher summer temperatures which may prove life-threatening. A 2003 heat wave in France with peak daytime temperatures of over 35 °C is estimated to have caused 14 800 excess deaths, particularly amongst the elderly (Pirard et al., 2005). In Greece, since the 1990s the level of sales of air-conditioning equipment has been sufficient to move the peak electricity demand from the winter to the summer.

In 2004 'cooling and ventilation' in the UK services sector used about 9 TWh of electricity, 4% of its total energy use (see Figure 1.3). Most of this was used in fan power rather than refrigeration. But is this energy use really necessary?

Analysis of the energy consumption of UK office buildings has shown a wide variation. A typical 'prestige' air-conditioned office can use nearly three times as much energy per square metre of floor area as a typical naturally ventilated one (Action Energy, 2003). In part this variation is due to different office functions. Even so, for a given type of office, those using 'good practice' design used 40% less energy than a 'typical' example. This will be discussed further in the next chapter.

Shallow plan or deep plan offices?

A key element of 'good practice' design is the use of shallow plan buildings. The LT (light and thermal) method (Baker and Steemers, 1992) gives a good description of its principles.

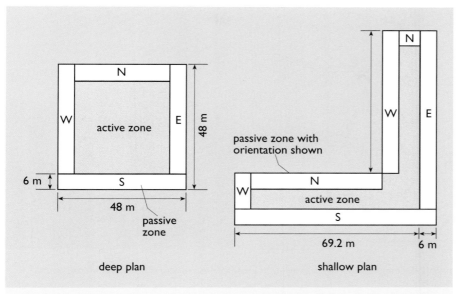

Figure 1.36 The LT method – a shallow plan design maximises the 'passive' zones that can be naturally lit and ventilated

For example, Figure 1.36 shows two alternative floor plans for an office design with 2304 m² of floor space, a 'deep plan' on the left and a 'shallow plan' on the right. There is a 'passive zone' extending approximately 6 m into the building all the way round that could make use of daylight and be naturally ventilated by opening the windows. The 'active zone' in the interior will require artificial lighting and is likely to need mechanical ventilation.

The shallow plan design minimises the area of the active zone and its electricity use, but at the cost of a longer external perimeter, increased wall area and a higher winter space heating energy loss. This increased heat loss is likely to be supplied by gas heating. When an overall primary energy analysis is carried out including the energy losses in electricity generation, the shallow plan design is estimated to use 10% less primary energy and lower CO_2 emissions than its deep plan counterpart.

Innovative natural ventilation

In many circumstances it may not be possible to use a shallow plan building. With careful design it is possible to ventilate a large building without resorting to the use of mechanical ventilation. Figures 1.37 and 1.38 show the Queen's Building at De Montfort University in Leicester, opened in 1993, and built with large vertical natural ventilation ducts. Warm air from the building, being less dense than the colder outside air, rises through these to be expelled through louvres at the top. These can be opened (under computer control) on different sides to make further use of the wind to suck air through the system. Air is drawn into the building on the ground and first floors.

The use of mechanical ventilation has been avoided but at the cost of a certain constraint of building design. It would be difficult, for example, to rearrange rooms for a different layout, something that regularly happens every three to ten years in conventional open plan offices (Santamouris, 1998).

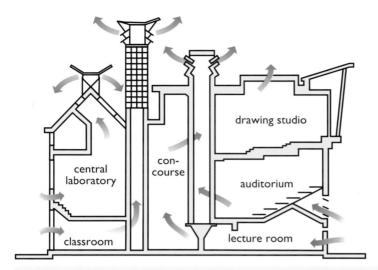

Figures 1.37 and 1.38 The Queen's Building, De Montfort University, Leicester, uses natural rather than mechanical ventilation

Efficient mechanical ventilation

Mechanical ventilation requires the use of electrically driven fans and ductwork to circulate air within a building. With **air conditioning**, the air can also be heated or cooled. In a domestic installation, the fans may only be rated at 50 watts in total and the ductwork will only be a few tens of metres in total length. In the system of a large multi-storey office or hospital (as shown in Figure 1.39), there may be a kilometre or more of steel ductwork usually hidden above a false ceiling (Figures 1.40 and 1.41). The fans may require large electric induction motors of 100 kW or more, which may run continously day and night 365 days a year.

If mechanical ventilation is necessary, there are ways to minimise the electricity consumption. For example, it is important to make sure that the ducts are large enough. A narrow duct may save on metalwork but will result in more fan power to pump the air. Fan motors offer a good opportunity for reducing electricity use, by:

- using a high-efficiency electric motor
- correct sizing of the motor
- using a variable speed drive.

High-efficiency electric motors

The use of high-efficiency electric motors is an important topic, not just restricted to mechanical ventilation. Overall about a half of UK electricity is used in motors of one sort or another. In the industrial sector it makes up two-thirds of the total use (ETSU, 1998). The comments below are thus of much wider relevance than just to energy in buildings.

For a fan motor, the load is the mechanical power output required for the fan to circulate air at the required rate, and the percentage efficiency of the motor can be expressed as

$$\frac{\text{load (kW)}}{\text{electric power input (kW)}} \times 100$$

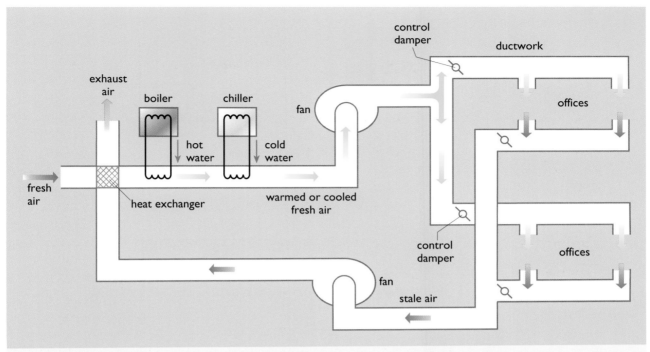

Figure 1.39 A typical mechanical ventilation/air-conditioning system of a large office building. Outside air is drawn in and passed through a heat recovery heat exchanger. It is then heated or cooled as required and blown into the building with a large fan. The flow into different sections is varied with flaps (control dampers). The exhaust air is then sucked out again with another fan to be blown through the heat exchanger and back to the outside air

Figure 1.40 A large commercial building may contain a kilometre or more of ductwork like this

Figure 1.41 All that is visible when the false ceiling is in place are the air vents

All induction motors (i.e. mains-driven ones) have inherent losses that reduce their efficiency. These motors run at constant speed but are required to deliver varying loads, so the way the losses depend on these two factors is very important. The main losses fall into two categories:

■ The most important losses for a motor running at full load are 'copper losses', the energy converted into heat as current flows in the coils. Larger loads mean higher currents, and these can account for an efficiency reduction of up to 10% at high loads.

■ There are also frictional and air drag losses in the motor, and 'iron losses' resulting from the constantly changing magnetic fields. These are not much affected by the load, so although they may account for only 3% of the total loss at full load, they can become very important at low loads, when the copper losses are small.

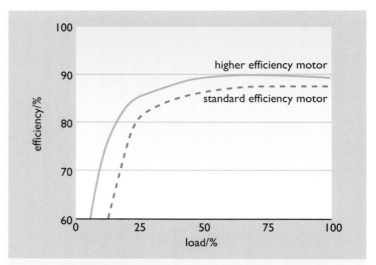

Figure 1.42 Efficiency as a function of load for a 7.5 kW motor (redrawn from ETSU, 1998)

Figure 1.42 shows the overall effect on motor efficiency for a standard efficiency 7.5 kW motor when plotted against load. It is most efficient at above 50% of full load, where the above two categories jointly contribute to a total loss of about 13% of the input power. At very low loads, the power required to overcome the iron and friction losses becomes significant and efficiency can fall off dramatically at below 25% full load.

The actual efficiency of a particular motor will depend on its size. Motors of 100 kW or more can reach efficiencies of 97%. Conversely the efficiency of small motors can be under 80% and the fall-off at low loads is much worse than shown in the figure.

These inefficiencies can all be reduced. Iron losses can be reduced by using better magnetic materials, friction and air drag by better rotor design and the copper losses by using thicker windings. Typically 'high efficiency' induction motors are about 3% more efficient at full load than their 'standard' counterparts, but as can be seen from Figure 1.42, the efficiency improvement at part load can be much more than this.

High-efficiency motors have a wide range of applications in buildings apart from driving fans, for example in lifts and central heating pumps. For low power applications, high-efficiency permanent magnet motors are becoming available, for example for domestic central heating pumps.

Correct motor sizing

Many motors are sized so that they have enough power to start up an application (be it a fan, a refrigerator or a piece of machinery), yet when they are actually running it they are using only a fraction of their full rating. This could lead to them running at low efficiency for most of the time. It is thus really important to make sure that motors aren't oversized.

Once running, the losses can be reduced by lowering the voltage to the windings. On large 3-phase motors this can be achieved by switching the arrangement of the windings. Alternatively, high voltage electronic switches (thyristors) can be used to reduce the voltage. At a smaller scale, this principle is used in the Savaplug, sold for use with domestic refrigerators. The full mains voltage is applied when the fridge compressor starts up, but once running the voltage is reduced. Savings of 20% are claimed.

Variable speed drives (VSDs)

Induction motors are locked into the mains frequency and usually run at 3000 rpm. This makes it difficult to vary the output of pumps or fans. It is thus common practice to set up a motor to drive a fan at the maximum flow rate and then to install restricting control dampers in the ductwork to vary the flow. This is somewhat like driving a car using only the brakes to control the speed.

A variable speed drive provides the solution by changing the *frequency* of the supply to the motor. VSDs became possible with the development of high voltage thyristor switches in the 1980s. The mains AC voltage is first rectified to DC. Then the thyristor switches convert this back to AC at the frequency required by the motor. (Similar devices are used in large wind turbines to generate current at the fixed frequency mains voltage while allowing a variable speed for the rotor).

Although the efficiency of the VSD may only be 95%, its use allows the motor and the pumps or fans that it drives to be run at closer to their optimum efficiency over a range of speeds.

Alternative methods of cooling buildings

There are a number of ways to cool a building avoiding some of the disadvantages of electric air conditioning. For example, absorption chillers can use waste heat from CHP plants instead of electricity, or the building can be cooled by circulating ventilation air at night when air temperatures are lower (see Box 1.12). If electric air conditioning is unavoidable, then its performance can be improved by using ground source heat pumps rather than air source ones, or 'off-peak' air conditioning can be used, making ice at night for cooling during the day.

Absorption chillers

As mentioned earlier, gas-fired refrigerators were once common in UK homes, but how can a hot flame produce cooling?

Absorption chillers use the fact that some chemicals are **hygroscopic**, i.e. they are extremely attracted to water. For example, in 1850, Frenchman Edmond Carré showed that if a flask of concentrated sulphuric acid is connected to a flask of water via a tube that only permits a flow of vapour, an extraordinary reaction takes place. Any water vapour that diffuses through the tube into the sulphuric acid flask is instantly absorbed in the acid. This reduces the pressure in both flasks, forcing the water to boil to produce yet more vapour. It can only do this by absorbing heat from its surroundings (and cooling down itself). As the vapour diffuses and is absorbed by the acid, the water boils away at progressively lower and lower temperatures and pressures and may eventually freeze.

This process was used for making ice in shops in the early twentieth century before the development of modern refrigerators. The concentrated sulphuric acid can then be reconstituted by heating it to drive off the water and then letting it cool down again before repeating the process. Thus high temperature heat (to separate the sulphuric acid and water) can be used to produce cooling when they recombine.

A modern commercial refrigeration plant is likely to use lithium bromide instead of sulphuric acid, but the principle is the same. Alternatively, ammonia can be used as the refrigerant and water as the absorber (a process invented by Edmond Carré's brother, Ferdinand, in 1859).

Absorption chillers only have a COP of approximately 0.7–1.2, lower than that of an electric heat pump. However, because they use a heat source, rather than electricity, they do not suffer from the primary energy losses at the power station. The process is even more attractive where it can use waste exhaust heat from a CHP plant. In the longer term, heat from concentrating solar collectors could be a possibility in really sunny climates.

BOX 1.12 **A low-energy office building**

Figure 1.43 The Elizabeth Fry Building
(courtesy University of East Anglia)

The Elizabeth Fry Building, completed in 1995, was commissioned by the University of East Anglia in Norwich. The basement contains large lecture rooms and the top three floors are occupied by offices for the staff. The building is highly insulated with 200 mm of insulation in the walls, 300 mm in the roof and triple-glazed low-e argon-filled windows. The building was made very airtight by paying great attention to detail at design stage. It is gas heated and mechanically ventilated by a system incorporating four heat recovery heat exchangers. Instead of electric heat pump cooling it used the Swedish Termodeck system of thick concrete floor slabs, which are hollow and can be cooled by circulating outside air through them at night.

The overall energy performance has been very good. Its electrical energy consumption in 1997 was only 61 kWh per square metre of floor area and its gas consumption (corrected for degree days) was 37 kWh m^{-2}. These figures compare very favourably with corresponding values of 128 kWh m^{-2} and 97 kWh m^{-2} for a good practice air-conditioned office building in the UK.

Adapted from Standeven et al., 1998.

1.5 **UK potential for savings**

As pointed out at the beginning of this chapter, the domestic and services sectors use over 40% of the UK's delivered energy. In 2005, out of the total UK annual CO_2 emissions of almost 153 MtC (million tonnes of carbon) the domestic sector contributed approximately 37 MtC and the services sector another 23 MtC (DTI, 2006b). The question is how much of these emissions could be saved by using the techniques described above.

1.5.1 **Domestic sector**

The PIU study

The potential for savings in the UK domestic sector has been studied in depth in recent years. A study by the Performance and Innovation Unit (now called the Prime Minister's Strategy Unit) suggested a total potential for energy savings of 1 EJ yr^{-1} in the existing stock (i.e. approximately 10% of UK primary energy use) (PIU, 2001). This would result in savings in carbon emissions of nearly 24 MtC^{-1}. Table 1.14 lists the options studied.

The 'economic potential' includes those options for which the **internal rate of return** (IRR) is greater than 6%. The IRR is the rate at which it would be worth borrowing money to finance the measure; the higher the rate, the more economic the measure. Those with an IRR of 6% or less were deemed to be uneconomic. The calculations ignore any extra credit for carbon emission savings (see *Costing Energy,* Book 1, Chapter 12 for more on economic evaluation).

There is a further 'technical potential' which could be achieved at a lower rate of return.

This is an impressive list. The total should be treated with some caution because there may be some double counting. For example if a building is insulated first, then the potential for savings with more efficient heating will be reduced.

A later study by the Building Research Establishment considered the options above in more detail (Shorrock et al., 2005), producing a similar answer to the PIU, but including 50 PJ yr^{-1} from floor insulation and a (relatively expensive) potential of over 70 PJ yr^{-1} from domestic photovoltaic (PV) installations.

The 40% house project

A study carried out by the Environmental Change Institute (ECI) at Oxford (Boardman et al., 2005) went further and looked at what would be required to achieve a 60% reduction in CO_2 emissions in the UK domestic sector by 2050.

Most controversially, rather than embarking on a large programme of insulating solid-walled buildings, it suggested that the housing demolition rates would have to increase dramatically. Around 14% of the current stock would need to have been replaced with energy-efficient buildings by 2050.

In addition to the measures considered above, it assumed a very large take-up of CHP, with 22% of dwellings having community heating. This is likely

Table 1.14 Energy savings and carbon emission reductions from domestic energy efficiency

Type of saving	Measure	Energy saving /PJ yr⁻¹	Carbon saving /MtC yr⁻¹	Internal rate of return
Economic potential				
Insulation	Loft insulation	71	1.4	16%
	Cavity wall insulation	134	2.6	32%
	Double glazing	88	1.7	19%
Heating systems	Condensing gas boilers	273	5.3	27%
	DHW cylinder insulation	17	0.3	200%
	Heating controls	21	0.4	38%
	Small-scale CHP	8	0.3	19%
Electricity	Energy-efficient lights	38	1.4	50%
	Appliances	80	2.9	19%
Subtotal of economic potential		731	16.3	
Percentage of domestic total		37%	41%	
Additional technical potential				
Insulation	Solid wall insulation	143	2.8	+3%
	Draught proofing	17	0.3	+6%
	High-performance glazing	63	1.2	−2%
Heating systems	New district heating CHP	25	0.9	not given
	Ground source heat pumps	17	0.7	0%
	Solar water heating	84	1.6	−8%
Subtotal of additional technical potential		349	7.7	
Total		1092	23.8	
Percentage of domestic total		54%	57%	

Source: PIU, 2001

to be most used in city centres and provides a way of cutting the energy use in historic buildings. Whitehall in London, for example, is currently supplied by a gas turbine CHP plant in the Admiralty. Outside city centres the ECI study assumed that a further 40% of dwellings would use domestic micro-CHP. It also assumed higher insulation levels, with wall U-values of 0.1 W m^{-2} K^{-1} and the use of high-efficiency triple glazing.

As for electricity use by appliances and lighting, the study only projected a 27% overall fall in national consumption from 1998 levels. While a fourfold reduction in electricity use seems possible in cold appliances and lighting, electricity use by TVs and consumer electronics could well double by 2050.

In order to reach the 60% target it, like the BRE study, included a large take-up of solar thermal water heating and PV panels. Even so, it was necessary to assume that the overall carbon intensity of electricity from the grid would fall by a quarter by 2050 through the use of more renewable energy.

1.5.2 Services sector

A study carried out for the Royal Commission on Environmental Pollution looked at the services sector (Fisher et al., 1998). It suggested that the economic energy-saving potential here was 22%, resulting in emission cuts of 5.1 MtC. Approximately 10% of this potential was through the use of small-scale CHP. It estimated that including the additional technical potential, the total potential was nearly double that, at 39%, with emission savings of 8.2 MtC.

1.6 Conclusions

This chapter has described a wealth of opportunities for saving energy in buildings. The economic potential in the domestic and commercial or services sectors, according to the PIU and RCEP studies, is approximately 0.9 EJ yr^{-1}. The technical potential is even higher, at around 1.4 EJ yr^{-1}. The bulk of this potential lies in heat energy savings through the large-scale application of very ordinary technologies: thicker insulation, double glazing and condensing gas boilers.

To achieve carbon emissions cuts of 60% from the UK building stock will need further steps. These might include digging up the streets to distribute waste heat from power stations to most city-centre buildings, or the development and deployment of millions of domestic micro-CHP units. It may even require the demolition of large numbers of 'energy-unfit' houses.

The technical potential for cutting electricity use is enormous, yet it does seem an uphill struggle against a tide of new devices which are designed to be 'attractive' and 'convenient' rather than 'energy efficient'.

Most importantly, we live in a culture where the provision of 'energy services' – buildings that are warm in winter and adequately lit – has been seen largely as a matter of supplying cheap gas and electricity. The needs of facing up to climate change and diminishing North Sea gas supplies seem to be changing attitudes to energy saving. This topic is discussed further in Chapter 3.

References

Action Energy (2003) *Energy Consumption Guide 19: Energy use in offices*, available from http://www.carbontrust.org.uk [Accessed 8 July 2006].

AEA Technology (2005) *The Validity of Food Miles as an Indicator of Sustainable Development, Final report produced for DEFRA*, downloadable from http://statistics.defra.gov.uk/esg/reports/foodmiles/final.pdf [Accessed 16 August 2005].

Association for Environment Conscious Building (AECB) (2005) *Gold and Silver Energy Performance Standards for Buildings*, AECB, available from www.aecb.net [Accessed 29 July 2006].

Baker, N.V. and Steemers, K. (1992) *The LT Method 2.0: An Energy Design Tool for Non-Domestic Buildings*, Cambridge, Cambridge Architectural Research Ltd.

Beggs, C. (2002) *Energy Management Supply and Conservation*, Elsevier, Oxford.

Boardman, B., Darby, S., Killip, G., Hinnells, M., Jardine, C.N., Palmer, J. and Sinden, G. (2005) *40% House*, Oxford, Environmental Change Institute.

Building Research Establishment (BRE) (2003) *The UK Potential for Community Heating with Combined Heat & Power*, available from http://www.est.org.uk/housingbuildings/communityenergy/ (in 'community energy publications') [Accessed 27 September 2006].

Building Research Establishment (BRE) (2005) *SAP 2005 – The Government's Standard Assessment Procedure for Energy Rating of Dwellings*, Building Research Establishment, Watford, BRE, available from http://www.projects.bre.co.uk/SAP2005 [Accessed 8 May 2006].

Building Research Establishment (BRE) (2006) *Domestic Energy Fact File 2006*, Building Research Establishment, Watford, BRE, available from http://www.bre.co.uk [Accessed 3 June 2006].

Carbon Trust (2005) Historical UK Degree Days Data, downloadable from http://www.carbontrust.co.uk/resource/degree-days/what_are.htm [Accessed 24 March 2007].

Danish Energy Authority (DEA) (2005) *Heat Supply in Denmark*, available from http://ens.netboghandel.dk/english/ (in 'publications') [Accessed 27 September 2006].

Danter, E. (1951) *A Survey of Temperatures in Houses*, Heating and Ventilating Engineer.

Department of Trade and Industry (DTI) (2000) *Digest of UK Energy Statistics (DUKES)*, HMSO.

Department of Trade and Industry (DTI) (2001) *Digest of UK Energy Statistics (DUKES)*, HMSO.

Department of Trade and Industry (DTI) (2003) *Energy Consumption in the UK*, available from http://www.dti.gov.uk/energy [Accessed 9 November 2006].

Department of Trade and Industry (DTI) (2005a) *Digest of UK Energy Statistics (DUKES),* HMSO.

Department of Trade and Industry (DTI) (2005b) *Woking Park PAFC CHP Monitoring,* available from http://www.dti.gov.uk/energy) [Accessed 27 September 2006].

Department of Trade and Industry (DTI) (2006a) *Energy Consumption in the UK – Consumption Tables,* available from www.dti.gov.uk/energy [Accessed 28 July 2006].

Department of Trade and Industry (DTI) (2006b) *Energy Sector Indicators 2006,* available from www.dti.gov.uk/energy [Accessed 29 June 2006].

Energy Saving Trust (EST) (2000) *Heat pumps in the UK– a monitoring report, GIR72,* available from http://www.est.org.uk [Accessed 27 September 2006].

Energy Saving Trust (EST) (2002) *Refurbishment site guidance for solid-walled houses – roofs,* Good Practice Guide 296, available from http:// www.est.org.uk, [Accessed 8 May 2006].

Energy Saving Trust (EST) (2005) *Best Practice in New Housing – a Practical Guide,* CE95, available from http://www.est.org.uk) [Accessed 27 September 2006].

Energy Saving Trust (EST) (2006) *Rise of the machines,* London, available from http://www.est.org.uk [Accessed 7 July 2006].

Energy Technology Support Unit (ETSU) (1998) *Energy Savings with Motors and Drives,* Good Practice Guide 2, available from www.carbontrust.co.uk) [Accessed 1 May 2006].

European Union (EU) (2005) *Directive 2005/32/EC Establishing a Framework for the Setting of Ecodesign Requirements for Energy Using Products,* available from http://ec.europa.eu/enterprise/eco_design/directive_2005_ 32.pdf, [Accessed 23 June 2006].

Feist, W., Peper, S., Kah, O. and von Oesen, M. (2005) *Climate Neutral Passive House Estate in Hannover – Kronsberg: Construction and Measurement Results,* Darmstadt, Germany, available from http://www. passivhaustagung.de/englisch/texte/PEP-Info1_Passive_Houses_Kronsberg. pdf [Accessed 30 July 2006]

Fisher J., Blyth, W., Collings, S., Boyle, S., Wilder, J., Henderson, G. and Grubb, M. (1998) *Prospects for Energy Saving and Reducing Demand for Energy in the UK,* London, Royal Commission on Environmental Pollution.

Glacier Bay (n.d.) *Vacuum Insulation Panels (VIPs) Principles, Performance and Lifespan,* California, Glacier Bay Inc., available from http://www.glacierbay.com/vacpanelinfo.asp [Accessed 24 June 2006].

House of Lords Science & Technology Committee (2005) *Energy Efficiency, 2nd Report of Session 2005–6,* available from http://www.parliament.uk [Accessed 1/05/2006].

International Energy Agency (IEA) (2005) *A Comparison of Distributed CHP/DH with Large-Scale CHP/DH*, London, IEA.

Luwoge (2006) *Das 3-Liter-Haus*, available from http://www.luwoge.de [Accessed 27 September 2006].

Nicholls, R. (2002) *Low Energy Design*, Interface Publishing, Oldham.

Nørgård, J. S. (1989) 'Low Electricity Appliances – Options for the Future', in Johansson, T. B. et al. (eds), *Electricity*, Sweden, Lund University Press.

Office of the Deputy Prime Minister (ODPM) (2001) *Conservation of Fuel and Power Approved Document L2, Buildings that are not Dwellings*, HMSO.

PB Power (2005) *The Supply of Heat from Barking Power Station to the Borough of Barking and Dagenham*, London, PB Power.

Performance and Innovation Unit (PIU) (2001) *Energy Efficiency Strategy*, London, UK Cabinet Office, available from http://www.strategy.gov.uk/downloads/files/PIUc.pdf [Accessed 1 July 2006].

Pirard P., Vandentorren, S., Pascal, M., Laaidi, K., LeTertre, A., Cassadou, S. and Ledrans, M. (2005) *Summary of the Mortality Impact Assessment of the 2003 Heatwave in France, Eurosurveillance*, vol. 10, available from http://www.eurosurveillance.org [Accessed 5 July 2006.

Royal Commission on Environmental Pollution (RCEP) (2000) *Energy – The Changing Climate*, London, The Stationery Office, http://www.rcep.org.uk/newenergy.htm [Accessed 1 September 2006].

Santamouris M. (1998) *Retrofitting: Technology Module 7, Solar Energy in European Office Buildings,* University College Dublin, available from http://www.erg.ucd.ie [Accessed 9 July 2006].

Shorrock, L.D., Henderson, J. and Uttley, J.I. (2005) *Reducing Carbon Emissions from the UK Housing Stock,* Watford, Building Research Establishment, available from www.bre.co.uk.

Society of British Gas Engineers (SBGI) (2003) *MicroCHP – delivering a low carbon future,* SBGI.

Standeven, M., Cohen, R., Bordass, B. and Learnan, A. (1998) 'PROBE 14: Elizabeth Fry Building', *Building Services Journal*, April, pp. 37–42; also available from http://www.usablebuildings.co.uk/Probe/FRY/FRYAPR98.PDF [Accessed 8 July 2006].

US Department of Environment (US DoE) (n.d.), *Properties of Fuels*, US Department of Energy Alternative Fuels Data Center, available from http://www.eere.energy.gov/afdc/pdfs/fueltable.pdf [Accessed 2 December 2006].

Weizsacker, E. von, Lovins, A.B. and Lovins, L.H. (1997) *Factor Four: Doubling Wealth – Halving Resource Use*, Earthscan.

Chapter 2

Quantifying the savings

by Bob Everett

2.1 **Introduction**

The previous chapter has described methods of saving energy, but how do we quantify the savings? Measuring energy supply is easy enough; electricity and gas can be recorded on appropriate meters, but assessing energy that has *not* been used is more difficult.

A key element is understanding how energy has been used. This may not be straightforward. Determining energy savings in houses and flats is made difficult by the wide range of occupant behaviour. There can be a fourfold difference in fuel bills in almost identical buildings caused by different numbers of occupants, different internal temperatures, window opening, appliance use, etc. Assessing the energy use of non-domestic buildings can be even more difficult. In offices there can be a twentyfold difference in energy costs per square metre of floor area between different buildings, in part due to their different uses.

The components of heating systems and appliances can all be tested in the laboratory. This has led to programmes of energy labelling and only permitting the sale of the most energy-efficient devices.

Testing whole buildings in a laboratory is very expensive. Although this is actually done for research into their fire resistance, testing their thermal performance is perhaps best done in the open, since they are expected to be subject to the forces of wind, rain and sun. There are a number of test methods that can be used, which will be described later.

Energy metering is an essential ingredient of understanding energy use, and in a large building the sub-metering of different functions may be necessary. Annual fuel bills can be compared with previous years and with standard energy use benchmarks to see if a building is to be considered energy-efficient or wasteful.

Since the oil price rises of the 1970s there has been research in many countries into energy use in buildings and ways to reduce it. The use of mathematical models is a key element in assessing the savings. This has been encouraged in the European Union by the recent Energy Performance of Buildings Directive (EPBD) (EU, 2002). This requires Member States to put in place:

- a methodology of calculation of the integrated energy performance of buildings
- a procedure for setting minimum energy standards in new and existing buildings
- the Energy Certification of large buildings, together with regular inspection of their heating and cooling installations.

2.1.1 **Energy models**

There are several types of energy model available:

1 Highly detailed building energy simulation models which take the physical description of the building fabric and its heating and lighting system as inputs. These are usually used for design purposes to give predictions of energy use and allow the initial sizing of heating or air-conditioning systems. These models are beyond the scope of this course.

2 Simpler models, based on the physical description of the building, used to give energy ratings and to show compliance with the UK Building Regulations and the EPBD. Examples of these are SAP (Standard Assessment Procedure) for dwellings and SBEM (Standard Building Energy Model) for non-domestic buildings. These can be used to produce Energy Label ratings for particular buildings and to estimate the benefits of various energy-saving measures.

3 Statistical regression models fitted to measured fuel bill data. These can be used to assess the actual performance and to set performance standards. They can be used as an aid to identifying malfunctioning equipment, and when improvements are made can give estimates of the energy savings based on measured data rather than assumed performance.

2.2 Energy labels for appliances

In 1994, following suggestions that the energy consumption of cold appliances on the European market could be reduced by up to 50%, the European Commission introduced a Directive requiring the energy usage of such appliances to be represented on the physical labelling. This labelling uses an A–G rating which reflects the consumption in kWh per litre of net volume. An A rated appliance uses about half of the electricity of an E rated one (Schiellerup, 2002). In 1999, a further Directive set minimum standards phasing out the sale of fridges with a rating below C (except for chest freezers where it could be E).

It must be said that the original labelling system was not very ambitious. At present (2006), many manufacturers offer not just A rated appliances but also A+ and even A++ ones that are more efficient than the rating system envisaged.

The labelling system has now been extended to a whole range of other appliances, for example washing machines, where the label also includes washing and spin dryer performance, water consumption and noise rating (see Figure 2.1).

Energy labels can also be found on lamps, electric ovens, air conditioners and even central heating pumps.

2.3 Testing buildings

There are a number of ways that the heat loss of buildings can be evaluated. One key method for new buildings is on-site inspection to see that insulation and vapour barriers are being properly installed. Other techniques include the use of thermographic cameras, pressure testing and thermal calibration.

2.3.1 Thermographic cameras

The heat losses from a building can be inspected using a thermographic camera. This converts radiated energy in the far infrared into visible images. Although the basic pictures are in 'black and white', they can be given false colour to stress the relative heat losses (see the cover of this book). Detailed inspection can show up building defects. For example, Figure 2.2 shows

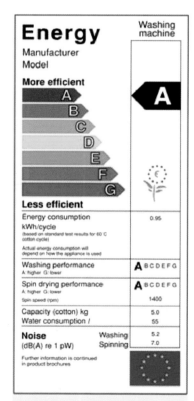

Figure 2.1 An energy label for a washing machine (DEFRA, 2004)

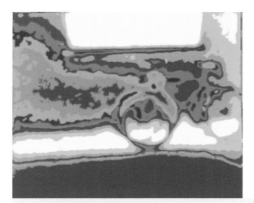

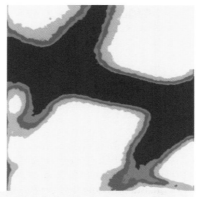

Figure 2.2 Thermographic image showing two bicycles leaning against the outside of a house lit by heat radiating out from a poorly insulated floor slab and a double-glazed window (cold is blue and hot is light yellow)

Figure 2.3 An internal thermographic image of a ceiling photographed from below showing the cold (blue) pattern of the ceiling joists with warm (yellow) insulated areas in between

heat losses through a window and the supposedly well-insulated floor slab of a house. The well-insulated wall appears dark. Figure 2.3 is an upward view inside the house, showing heat losses through the thermal bridging caused by insulation only being placed between ceiling joists. A cure for this would be to put more insulation over the top of them (as shown in Figure 1.8 in the previous chapter).

2.3.2 Pressure tests

These can be used to test the airtightness of a building. Usually one of the doors is replaced with a frame carrying a calibrated electric fan (see Figure 2.4). This blows large amounts of air into the building, in order to set up a standard pressure difference between the inside and outside of 50 Pa. This is roughly equivalent to the effects of a gale-force wind. The overall air leakage rate of the building at this pressure difference is usually expressed in cubic metres per hour per square metre of building envelope area (i.e. area of walls, roof, etc.).

For example, the design of the Elizabeth Fry Building mentioned in the previous chapter specifically required good airtightness. When tested it was found to have a leakage rate which was roughly five times better than a similar building without an airtightness specification. Problem areas (such as the revolving entrance doors) can be investigated using a small smoke generator allowing the air leakage to be clearly seen.

The 2006 Building Regulations now require that sample pressure tests are carried out as part of the on-site quality assurance checks for new houses.

2.3.3 Thermal calibration

Housing research field trials sometimes measure the total fabric and ventilation heat loss. This can be done by heating an unoccupied house for a period of a week or more and comparing the heating energy used with the average inside–outside temperature difference (for example, see Bell

Figure 2.4 A blower door being used to pressurise a building

and Lowe, 1998). The procedure has to make allowances for free heat gains from solar radiation that are always going to be present. This procedure is not widely used because it is very time-consuming.

2.4 Modelling the energy use of houses and flats

The need for an energy model to assess housing energy use and help with advice on energy-saving measures was identified in the UK in the 1980s. The Building Research Establishment developed a Domestic Energy Model (BREDEM) during the 1990s. This is essentially a simple degree-day model, using the techniques described in the previous chapter. It was checked against the results of field trials for low-energy houses and fuel bill surveys of older ones.

2.4.1 Standard Assessment Procedure (SAP)

One version of the BREDEM model has been used to form the core of SAP and it is now the calculation tool to show compliance with the Building Regulations for houses and flats. It is concerned only with the building and (apart from some aspects of lighting) not with appliances or the occupant behaviour. It thus assumes 'average' figures for such things as internal temperatures and hot water use.

Calculation procedure

The model basically uses the following calculation procedure:

1 First, the total fabric heat loss coefficient is calculated from the dwelling dimensions and the U-values of the various fabric elements such as the walls, windows, etc., as described in Box 1.4 of Chapter 1.

2 The ventilation heat loss coefficient, using an estimated ventilation rate, is then added. This then gives a total heat loss coefficient for the dwelling.

3 The 'free heat gains' are estimated, using 'average' assumptions on internal gains from occupants, appliances and hot water use. Solar gains and lighting energy use are calculated, based on the size and position of windows. These free heat gains are then used to determine a suitable degree-day base temperature as shown in Figure 1.18 in Chapter 1.

4 The net space heating load (i.e. that which will have to be supplied by the heating system) is then calculated using standard degree days for the central UK, adjusted to the chosen base temperature.

5 The efficiency of the heating system is determined by a very detailed assessment of the precise type, its fuel, the provision of controls, etc. This may well refer to the SEDBUK database for the efficiency of specific boilers (see Chapter 1). The fuel requirement for space heating can then be found.

6 The fuel needed for hot water is calculated using standard assumptions about usage.

7   Using 'average' asssumptions about appliance use, the overall electricity consumption can be calculated.

8   Summing items (5)–(7) gives the total dwelling energy use.

9   The annual CO_2 emission rate is calculated from the fuels used and their CO_2 emission factors (see Box 1.8 in Chapter 1).

The basic calculation method is set out as a six-page worksheet. However, the need to deal with all possible types of house and flat and their heating systems requires a large amount of explanatory material and many supplementary tables.

Model outputs

The present edition, SAP 2005 (BRE, 2005), has four key outputs:

- the energy consumption per unit floor area
- an energy cost rating (the SAP rating) based on this energy consumption
- the dwelling CO_2 emission rate (DER)
- an environmental impact rating (EIR), based on the annual CO_2 emissions.

The SAP rating

The SAP rating itself is essentially based on the cost of energy for space and water heating, ventilation and lighting. It is adjusted for floor area so that it is independent of dwelling size for a given built form. It is expressed on a scale of 1 to 100; the higher the number, the lower the running costs.

For example a pre-1919 house with solid walls, no loft insulation and no central heating would have a SAP rating of just over 20. A new house meeting the 2006 Building Regulations for England and Wales would have a SAP rating of about 85. Its fuel costs per square metre of floor area would be about a fifth of those for the older uninsulated house. Since the rating is based on cost, electrically heated houses will tend to have worse SAP ratings than gas heated ones.

The rating also allows for houses to have their own generation technologies, such as solar water heaters, PV panels or micro-CHP units. A house with zero net energy cost will have a rating of 100 and a figure of more than 100 is possible for those which actually export power.

SAP is not the only rating system using the BREDEM model. Another, the National Home Energy Rating (NHER) is widely used for assessing buildings in slightly more detail. One key difference is that it allows for local variations in degree days.

Carbon dioxide emissions

Compliance with the Building Regulations for new houses is now a matter of the dwelling emission rate (DER) meeting a minimum CO_2 emission target. The actual form of this is a little complicated (see BRE, 2006 for further details). The Environmental Impact Rating (EIR), like the SAP, is expressed on a scale of 1–100; the higher the number, the better the standard.

Home energy performance certificates

From June 2007 most UK house and flat sales and flat will require a Home Information Pack (HIP). This will require an energy survey (by a qualified inspector) and an up-to-date energy certificate. For these, the above ratings will be simplified into A–G bands (see Table 2.1)

Table 2.1 Rating bands for dwellings

SAP or EIR rating	Label band
≥92	A
81–91	B
69–80	C
55–68	D
39–54	E
21–38	F
1–20	G

Thus a new house complying with the 2006 regulations is likely to get a SAP B rating and the old, uninsulated house mentioned above might just get an F rating.

The average SAP rating for houses in England in 2001 has been estimated at 51 (an E rating on the scale above). Figure 2.5 shows an estimate of the distribution of ratings across the housing stock in England. The worst ratings are in private rented dwellings, where just under 12% in the sector had a SAP of 20 or less. It is estimated that a transformation of the overall housing stock to a SAP rating of 70 might reduce the CO_2 emissions by a third (DETR, 2000).

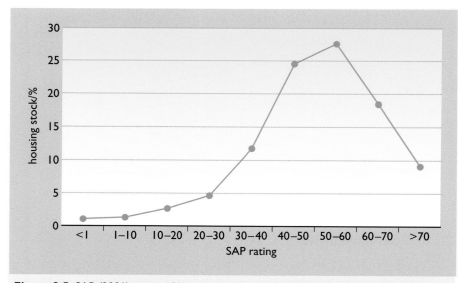

Figure 2.5 SAP (2001) rating of housing stock in England. Note that a revision to the SAP calculation procedure since 2001 means that this diagram slightly overstates the percentage of dwellings in the top categories in the current SAP 2005 system (source: ODPM, 2003)

2.5 **Modelling and assessing non-domestic buildings**

As mentioned above, there can be an enormous difference in energy use between different office buildings.

A small office building may be very similar to a house: cellular in form (i.e. with individual separate office rooms) and naturally ventilated. Its 'office equipment' may consist of a few telephones and PC computers, and it might be used for perhaps eight hours a day, five days a week.

At the other extreme, the prestige city offices of banks or insurance companies are often in large, air-conditioned buildings, are likely to include computer rooms, staff dining facilities, etc., and parts might be in almost continuous use. Between these extremes, there are naturally ventilated open-plan offices and 'standard' air-conditioned offices.

A considerable amount of work has gone into surveying UK office buildings to establish 'typical' energy use and also what constitutes 'good practice'. Since offices are more electricity intensive than houses, it is useful to look at their energy use in terms of their CO_2 emissions. Figure 2.6 shows the breakdown of CO_2 emissions for the four different categories of office buildings, giving both a 'typical' and 'best practice' example.

In a naturally ventilated cellular office, the CO_2 emissions for heating may make up half of the total, but in a prestige air-conditioned one they may be only one-sixth and actually be less than those for cooling and running ventilation fans.

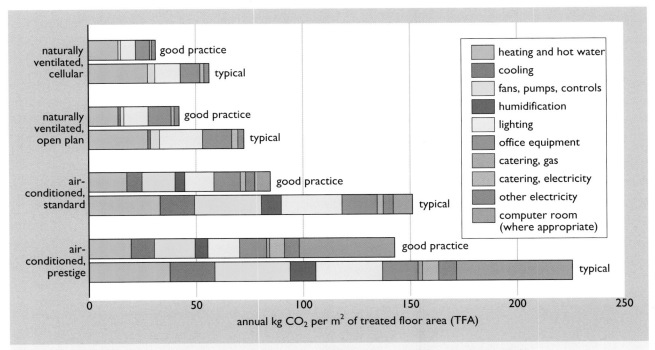

Figure 2.6 CO_2 emissions per square metre of floor area for different office types (Action Energy, 2003)

Any assessment of an actual building will require metering of the different areas of energy use. In a large building this may be carried out as part of the function of a computerised 'building management system' (BMS) which will also control the overall heating and ventilation system.

Measured figures, expressed in terms of energy per square metre of floor area and CO_2 emissions per square metre of floor area can be compared with published benchmarks, which are available for a wide range of different buildings.

This process of breaking down the energy use into different areas and categorising them is carried further in the Simplified Building Energy Model (SBEM) which will be used for preparing Energy Labels for large non-domestic buildings (ODPM, 2006). At the time of writing (July 2006) this is still under development.

2.5.1 Practical energy monitoring and targeting

In practice the energy manager of a large building will always have to ask the basic question: Why is energy wasted? There are many answers:

- Poorly designed buildings and installations. Buildings may be poorly insulated, resulting in high space heating costs, or mechanical ventilation ducts may be undersized so that fan power consumption is high

- Inadequate or poor control settings. For example, time clock controllers may be incorrectly set so that buildings are heated when not in use

- Inefficient plant operation, often arising from the use of old or out of date technology, a situation often made worse by poor maintenance

- Poor operating and working practices. Lights are often left on in buildings when they should be switched off.

If improvements are made, then, no doubt, the company's accountants will want to be assured that energy savings have actually been achieved and that any expenditure was cost effective. Comparing one year's fuel bills before the improvements with another's afterwards will give an answer. This may be obscured by differences in the weather between the years, or changes in business activity. It is most important to determine a firm baseline performance of how energy is currently used, before embarking on programmes of improvements. Even this can be quite difficult, because the energy consumption of a building will vary with the weather and occupant behaviour.

Time-dependent energy analysis

If enough detailed data can be gathered it is possible to produce a simple graph in which monthly energy consumption is plotted against time. This can show general trends and seasonal patterns in energy use. Figure 2.7 shows the gas consumption of a large building for the years 2001 and 2002.

It can be seen from this graph that:

- there is a large difference in monthly gas use from summer to winter

- there is a small base load gas use in summer, presumably for water heating and catering.

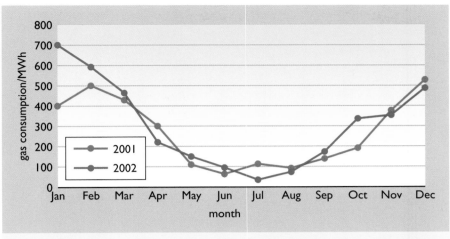

Figure 2.7 Monthly gas consumptions for 2001 and 2002 (source: Carbon Trust, 2006)

It also shows that the gas usage in January 2002 is much higher than in January 2001 and that usage for October 2002 is higher than for October 2001. Plotting out the monthly gas consumption for the two years together with the relevant degree days, as shown in Figure 2.8, reveals that January and October 2002 were cold months, with a large number of degree days. This is thus likely to be the main reason for the high gas usage, rather than some other factor, such as an increase in workload requiring use for an increased number of hours.

Linear regression analysis

It was suggested in Chapter 1 that the heat loss from a building should be proportional to the number of degree days, and Figure 2.8 seems to support this view. Assuming that there is a steady base heat load for hot

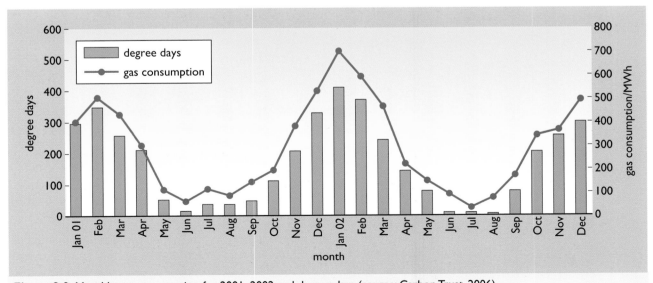

Figure 2.8 Monthly gas consumption for 2001–2002 and degree days (source: Carbon Trust, 2006)

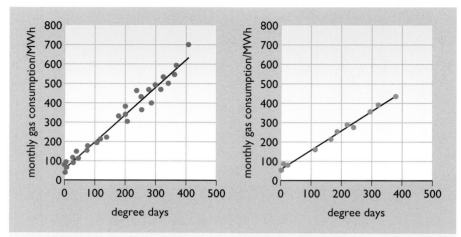

Figure 2.9 Baseline regression of building gas consumption against degree days over January 2001 to April 2003 showing measured data and fitted line y = 1.42 × degree days + 53.9 (source: Carbon Trust, 2006)

Figure 2.10 After improvements – gas consumption May 2003 to April 2004 with fitted line y = 1.02 × degree days + 56.7. This shows the reduced winter gas consumption (source: Carbon Trust, 2006)

water etc., there should then be a simple relationship between heating fuel consumption and degree days:

monthly fuel consumption = A × monthly degree days + B

where

A is a constant relating fuel consumption to degree days

B is the constant monthly base load.

A graph with monthly degree days as the x-axis and monthly heating energy as the y-axis should therefore be a straight line cutting the y-axis at B. (If there are zero degree days, the fuel consumption is the base load.) Figure 2.9 shows a possible graph. Notice that the actual dates no longer enter here; the graph just uses the pairs of fuel and degree-day values, regardless of when these were obtained. It shows that the base load, when there are no degree days, is about 50 MWh per month, and that gas use rises more or less linearly with degree days to 620 MWh per month for 400 degree days per month.

Linear regression analysis is a technique that analyses such data to:

- find how well it fits a **standard performance line**, and evaluate the constants A and B
- identify and investigate unexpected deviations from this performance line
- identify changes following alterations (in the building, the heating system, etc.)

It is a standard statistical procedure available in spreadsheet packages. Given two sets of paired data, such as the monthly gas consumption and degree days here, a spreadsheet can be used to plot a graph and give values A and B, fitting the 'best' straight line through the points. This is shown in the caption of Figure 2.9, where $A = 1.42$ MWh per degree day and $B = 53.9$ MWh.

Although used here for heating energy and degree days, the technique can equally be used to relate electricity use for lighting to the number of hours of occupancy or, in a factory, the energy use to the number of units of production.

The **standard performance line** allows the current energy use of the building to be compared with its past performance. Extending the line into the future (by entering monthly degree-day values into the line's equation) gives a prediction of how much energy the building would be expected to use if it continued to operate as it had done in the past.

If there is any persistent deviation from the historic performance line, it means that something has changed in the way that the building uses energy. Such deviations may result from changes in building use, or control settings, the installation of energy-efficiency measures, or malfunctioning equipment. The performance line therefore provides the benchmark by which to pick up these changes, be alerted to defects and to make judgements about them (such as how important they are and the magnitude of their effects).

For example, in the summer of 2003 the boiler plant and controls in the building shown in Figure 2.9 were replaced. The monthly gas consumption over the winter of 2003/4 is shown plotted in Figure 2.10, together with a new fitted performance line. This shows that there has been little change in the summer base load gas consumption, but the slope of the regression line has fallen dramatically. Had there been a cold month with 400 degree days, it is likely that the building would only have used 46.5 MWh instead of 62.0 MWh before the improvements.

The two regression lines can be used with long-term degree-day averages for the particular area to work out the overall energy savings and thus the cost effectiveness of the improvements.

For example, if the long-term average number of degree days over the year was 2000, then predictions of the long-term gas usage of the building would be given by:

annual gas use before improvements
$= 1.42 \times 2000 + 12 \times 53.9 = 3487$ MWh

annual gas use after improvements
$= 1.02 \times 2000 + 12 \times 56.7 = 2720$ MWh

annual energy saving $= 3487 - 2720 = 767$ MWh

If everything is in proper working order it should be expected that the building will continue to follow its performance line. There may be small deviations but any systematic departure should be investigated. These can be indicated by a technique known as 'cumulative sum of the difference' (CUSUM). This is beyond the scope of this course, but its details will be found in standard texts on energy monitoring and targeting (such as Carbon Trust, 2006).

Figure 2.11 Domestic two-tariff electricity meter and radio time switch

2.6 **Metering, tariffs and feedback**

Although sophisticated numerical analysis, such as that above, can be carried out if detailed fuel bills are available, it must be said that most gas and electricity metering has not yet caught up with 'the information age'. The basic 'spinning disk' meter (see Figure 2.11) was actually introduced at the end of the nineteenth century. The Board of Trade 'unit' of electricity was also defined as being the kilowatt-hour at the same time. Gas meters have only recently progressed from a mid-nineteenth century design using a set of bellows to drive a dial, to using ultrasonic waves to measure the flow through a pipe. Meters are usually read only once a year and customers are presented with estimated bills for the rest of the year. Thus most consumers are not really aware of the finer details of their energy use.

The coarse nature of metering also influences the tariffs under which gas and electricity are sold. Gas is basically supplied at a fixed price per kilowatt-hour throughout the year. In the past, tariffs have had a 'standing charge' to cover the cost of connection and metering. These have largely been replaced by a higher charge for a specified minimum amount of energy use per year. For example, a sample UK domestic gas tariff at the time of writing (July 2006) for prices including VAT reads:

First 5860 kWh per year   4.256p kWh^{-1}

Each additional kWh   2.678p kWh^{-1}

Given the current competitive energy market, gas prices for larger users are negotiable and are likely to be lower than the figures shown above. Large industrial consumers can also opt to buy gas at a cheaper 'interruptible' rate, but this supply can be disconnected at times of peak demand (usually with a few days' prior notice).

Electricity tariffs are more complex. Most domestic customers are on a 'two-tier' tariff similar to the gas one above. For example, sample VAT inclusive prices are:

First 900 kWh per annum   15.74p kWh^{-1}

All other kWh   9.60p kWh^{-1}

A more complex tariff is the 'Economy 7' one which also offers seven hours of cheap electricity at night (usually with a slightly higher daytime rate). The particular seven hours chosen is flexible and controlled by the National Grid company. In the UK the meter, along with any night storage heaters, is usually switched between the day and night rates by a radio-controlled time switch (shown on the right in Figure 2.11). This technology (introduced in the early 1980s) uses an inaudible subcarrier on the three long-wave Radio 4 transmitters. A sample domestic Economy 7 tariff (including VAT) reads:

First 1000 daytime kWh per quarter   17.29p kWh^{-1}

All other daytime kWh   10.37p kWh^{-1}

Night kWh   4.15p kWh^{-1}

This obviously gives a considerable incentive to shift electrical demand from the day to the night.

A commercial electricity tariff is likely to be even more complex. As with gas, large users can negotiate the price tariff terms, so they are likely to have lower average unit rates. However the tariff is likely to contain a 'maximum demand' element, very high prices indeed at times of peak demand on weekday winter evenings. Any commercial assessment of energy savings needs to take these into account.

2.6.1 Smart meters

The future of metering, particularly electricity metering, is quite a complex one. There are several possibilities for future 'smart' meters:

- **Clear general energy use information** – if customers had clear instantaneous feedback on their electricity use, then they might be able to take action to reduce their total consumption. Without it, they will remain ignorant.

- **Peak demand tariffs and information for all customers** – in the UK, the peak demand for electricity occurs between about 17:00 and 20:00 on winter weekdays. This is a time when offices and industry are shutting down for the day and domestic electricity consumers are arriving home, cooking meals and watching TV. Although part of this peak demand can be met from pumped storage plant, much of it has to be met from generation plant that will sit idle for most of the rest of the year. Although commercial electricity meters have a 'maximum demand' facility to discourage use, this is not present in domestic meters or tariffs. Experiments in California have shown an average peak demand reduction of 13% where customers were given warning of 'super-peak' prices (45p kWh^{-1}). This is a matter of 'shifting demand' and delaying such activities as washing clothes to a time of lower electricity prices.

- **Import–export metering for microgeneration** – the development of domestic micro-CHP and PV panels brings with it the need for two-way metering and billing for both imported and exported electricity.

- **Remote scheduling of domestic micro-CHP and appliance use** – on-peak/ off-peak meters are already remotely radio-controlled. It is only a short step to foresee a fully 'informated grid', where there is a parallel two-way flow of information about electricity use and generation. Thus if a load were deemed to be relatively unimportant, it would not be supplied until the electricity price had fallen to an appropriate level or a certain amount of time had elapsed. Domestic micro-CHP plant could also be remotely controlled to generate on demand rather than just meeting the heat needs of their particular house. It has also been suggested that an 'informated grid' could give rise to whole new decentralised markets for electricity (Awerbuch, 2004).

At present the capital cost of 'smart meters' appears to be a stumbling block. There is a perverse logic to this – if buildings can be made to consume little energy, then it does not make much sense to pay for expensive meters to measure it. On the other hand, if these meters allow the flexible use of limited energy supplies, it may be money well worth spending.

References

Action Energy (2003) *Energy Consumption Guide 19: Energy Use in Offices*; also available online at http://www.carbontrust.org.uk [Accessed 8 July 2006].

Awerbuch, S. (2004) *Restructuring our electricity networks to promote decarbonisation*, Tyndall Centre Working Paper 49; also available online at http://www.tyndall.ac.uk/publications/pub_list_2004.shtml [Accessed 3 October 2006].

Bell, M. and Lowe, R.J. (1998) *The York Energy Demonstration Project: Final Report. CeBE report no. 3*. Centre for the Built Environment, Leeds Metropolitan University, Leeds, UK.

Building Research Establishment (BRE) (2005) *SAP 2005 – The Government's Standard Assessment Procedure for Energy Rating of Dwellings*, Watford, BRE; also available online at http://www.projects.bre.co.uk/SAP2005 [Accessed 8 May 2006].

Building Research Establishment (BRE) (2006) *Part L explained: The BRE Guide*, Watford, Building Research Establishment.

Carbon Trust (2006), *Degree Days for Energy Management – a Practical Introduction, Good Practice Guide 310*; also available online at http://www.carbontrust.org.uk [Accessed 14 July 2006].

Department for Environment, Food and Rural Affairs (DEFRA) (2004) *Energy Labels: Helping you Make the Right Choice*; also available online at http://www.defra.gov.uk/environment/consumerprod/energylabels/energylabel.pdf [Accessed 12 July 2006].

Department of the Environment, Transport and the Regions (DETR) (2000) *English House Condition Survey, 1996: Energy Report*, London, DETR.

European Parliament (2002), *Directive 2002/91/EC on the Energy Performance of Buildings*; also available online at http://www.managenergy.net/products/R210.htm [Accessed 18 July 2006].

Office of the Deputy Prime Minister (ODPM) (2003) *English House Condition Survey, 2001: Building the Picture*, London; also available online at http://www.communities.gov.uk [Accessed 20 July 2006].

Office of the Deputy Prime Minister (ODPM) (2006) *A User Guide to iSBEM: An interface for SBEM (Simplified Building Energy Model)* Office of the Deputy Prime Minister, London; also available online at http://www.bre.co.uk [Accessed 3 October 2006].

Schiellerup, P. (2002) *An Examination of the Effectiveness of the EU Minimum Standard on Cold Appliances: the British Case*, Oxford, Environmental Change Institute; also available online at http://www.eci.ox.ac.uk/lowercf/pdfdownloads/ECEEE01_PS.pdf [Accessed 3 October 2006].

Standeven, M., Cohen, R., Bordass, B. and Learnan, A. (1998) 'PROBE 14: Elizabeth Fry Building', *Building Services Journal*, April, pp. 37–42; also available online at http://www.usablebuildings.co.uk/Probe/FRY/FRYAPR98.PDF [Accessed 8 July 2006].

Chapter 3

Policies for managing energy use

by Horace Herring

3.1 Introduction

In the previous chapters we have seen there is a large technical and economic potential for energy efficiency. But will people take up that potential? This chapter outlines what policies a government can enact to enable people to fulfil the efficiency potential, and examine the barriers to people reducing their energy use.

Before people will act they have to be convinced there is a problem and a feasible solution. The problem is climate change and the government's solution is to reduce CO_2 emissions by 60% by 2050 through a programme of energy-efficiency improvements and switch to low-carbon energy sources. Buildings account for over 40% of UK CO_2 emissions, so they must play their part in these reductions, primarily through much greater energy efficiency leading to reduced consumption.

If people accepted the problem and agreed with the solution then, given the large potential for savings and the long timescale, the 60% target could be achieved (Shorrock et al., 2005). However there is no unanimous political, let alone scientific, agreement on the problem or the solutions. This is not unusual, as the spectrum of responses to such environmental problems may be summed up as follows:

- denial – it's media hype
- indifference – 'it doesn't affect me' or 'it's someone else's problem'
- laissez-faire – 'it will work itself out' or 'it will solve itself' (or 'leave it to the market')
- technical fix – 'technology will solve the problem' (i.e. what Chapter 1 is about)
- government regulation – 'the government will do something' (like standards, subsidies, etc.)
- behavioural change – 'we should change our behaviour and adopt a sustainable lifestyle'.

This chapter accepts the existence of the problem and the need for the government action, so concentrates on the last two of these points. What can the government do, and what can we do?

BOX 3.1 Definitions of energy efficiency, energy conservation and energy intensity, Factor 4

The concept of 'energy services' – services that energy uniquely can provide, such as comfortable homes and working environments, hot water for washing, adequate lighting, etc., was introduced in Chapter 1.

Energy savings brought about by the reduction in consumption of energy services are usually considered to be due to 'energy conservation', while savings achieved without a reduction in energy services are considered to be due to 'energy efficiency'. As the Royal Commission on Environmental Pollution (RCEP) remarked, 'energy conservation ... implies reductions in the consumption of energy services. That could be achieved simply by 'making do' with less energy – by turning thermostats down and tolerating lower temperatures, for instance' (RCEP, 2000, p. 85).

Energy efficiency, however, involves 'obtaining more useful heat, light or work from each unit of energy supplied, either as a result of technological improvements or by reducing waste; in other words, obtaining the same services with less use of energy'

The concept of energy efficiency can only be meaningfully applied to a specific piece of equipment (like a boiler or an engine) where energy inputs and (energy service) outputs can be directly measured.

$$\text{Energy efficiency} = \frac{\text{energy service output}}{\text{energy input}}$$

For example, for a lamp, the energy service output is its light in lumens. We can say that its energy efficiency is its *efficacy* in lumens per watt (see Chapter 1). For a car, the energy service output can be taken as the number of miles travelled. Its energy efficiency will then be in miles per gallon (see Book 3, *Managing Transport Energy*).

The terms 'energy intensity' and 'specific energy consumption' (SEC) are also used. These are the inverse of energy efficiency.

$$\text{Energy intensity or specific energy consumption} = \frac{\text{energy input}}{\text{energy service output}}$$

So for a car, the specific energy consumption can be expressed in litres per 100 km travelled.

The energy intensity of a fridge can be described in terms of the annual energy used per unit of cold storage volume, the basis of their energy labelling (see Chapter 2). For houses or offices it might be annual energy used per unit of floor area. This is the basis of the SAP (for domestic buildings) and SBEM (for non-domestic buildings) ratings. For a particular industry it might be expressed in terms of physical output, GJ per tonne of steel produced.

For a whole economy, the energy intensity can be expressed in terms of the amount of energy used per £ of Gross Domestic Product generated.

A doubling of energy efficiency is a halving of energy intensity.

'Factor 4' is a phrase coined by energy-efficiency enthusiasts, to describe the possibility of doubling wealth but halving energy use, that is, achieving a fourfold increase in energy efficiency – or a 75% reduction in energy intensity (Weizsacker et al., 1997). A more extreme version of this idea is 'Factor 10', that is, achieving a tenfold increase in energy efficiency (or a 90% reduction in energy intensity).

3.2 Consumers and efficiency

The current drive of UK government energy-efficiency policy is to reduce CO_2 emissions from buildings. Books 1 and 2 have described how the carbon intensity of the energy supply can be reduced, through the use of natural gas, nuclear power or renewable energy. Chapters 1 and 2 have described various technological options for reducing the energy demand in the building stock. These are not the whole story. There are also individual and societal factors that determine overall energy consumption (see Figure 3.1). Here the carbon emissions are a result of three factors that interact. Books 1 and 2 covered carbon intensity. Chapter 1 of this block was about household-level factors and this chapter concentrates on individual and societal factors, especially the energy services required.

The number of households is a key factor in energy use. As pointed out in Chapter 1, owing to the continuing reduction in household size, the number

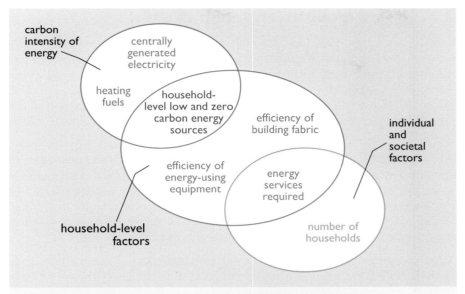

Figure 3.1 Key factors determining UK residential sector carbon emissions (source: Boardman et al., 2005)

of households is rising faster than the UK population, so the number of appliances, such as refrigerators, is expected to rise substantially.

Another crucial determinant of energy use is consumer behaviour. The energy labels for appliances described in Chapter 2 are based on use under 'average' conditions. But there can be wide variations in use for identical appliances, depending upon the conditions under which they operate. A fridge placed next to a cooker or boiler will use more than one in a garage. A freezer whose door is left open or that is not defrosted regularly will use more. A washing machine may use a specific amount of energy per wash, but the total annual energy consumption will be dependent on the particular demand for that energy service, i.e. the amount of washing chosen to be done.

Saving energy is not just about technology but about our habits, attitudes and lifestyle. Hence energy-efficient technologies may not achieve their full energy saving potential, since consumers often change the way they operate efficient devices, i.e. use them longer, more intensively, or buy more of them.

Whilst the two previous chapters have examined ways to reduce energy use through technology, this chapter examines ways to reduce our energy use through changing our behaviour. This can be at an individual level, by getting us to change our small 'wasteful' habits, like leaving lights on or overfilling the kettle. Or it can be at the community level, like taking part in DIY solar heating or car-sharing schemes. Or it can be at the national level, where the government tries to change our energy use, through regulations such as speed limits or appliance standards, or incentives such as grants for insulation and micro-CHP systems. Finally, in the future, there might even be rationing schemes, where the amount of energy you can use is limited.

So technology on its own is not the answer. It has to be combined with suitable government (or society) policies and individual actions before we can achieve significant energy (or carbon) savings.

3.2.1 Getting our attention

Consumers are bombarded by advertisements on how to save money and cut costs – cheaper motor insurance is just a phone call away, get interest on your current account through internet banking, collect coupons in the paper to get special offers at the supermarket. Consumer groups and even government agencies do calculations that reveal how consumers nationally could save hundreds of millions of pounds if they took advantage of the best offers.

Amidst all this advertising to be more efficient, to cut your costs and to save money are ads for another product: energy efficiency. Again we are informed of the large savings we could make (with just a little effort) and the 2006 *Energy Review* asserts that the UK could save tens of millions of tonnes of CO_2 (and many hundreds of millions of pounds) if only consumers used energy more efficiently (DTI, 2006a, paragraph 2.5)

Most consumers pay little heed to the vast majority of these ads to save money. However some ads are very successful, particularly those that only involve a one-off effort like making a phone call, such as purchasing car insurance by phone or ordering goods over the internet. Those that involve (or are perceived to involve) more substantial effort, like changing bank accounts, are less successful. Finally those that may involve a change in behaviour: drinking less, driving more slowly, eating better, are the least successful.

The reasons why consumers do not respond to measures that are in their economic interest are a subject of deep concern to policymakers, a field of study for academics and a cause of anguish to advertisers. A superficial response is to blame the consumers for being irrational, lazy, uninterested in saving money, apathetic, etc. While individual consumers may be any of these things, it is a great mistake to believe that any group of consumers, like the old, the young, the unemployed, single parents, women, men, etc. has these characteristics. If the people do not heed our message, the problem probably lies with the message, not the people. Thus when consumers do not respond to the energy-efficiency message and behave (in the 'experts' view) 'economically irrationally' the answer is not to question their rationality but to understand their behaviour (Princen et al., 2002).

3.2.2 Market barriers

People are saturated with adverts every day to buy this or do that. Even if they agree with the message – and few dispute the merits of cutting costs and saving money – their time is limited and they have to set priorities for action. It is basically the 'hassle factor' – how much effort is involved in changing banks, getting a quote by phone, buying an energy-efficient light bulb? People subject their effort to a crude cost-benefit analysis: what will I save for this effort, is it worth the hassle? Academics refer to this hassle as 'transaction costs' and often these present a formidable obstacle to achieving action.

Are five minutes on the phone worth saving £50 on the motor insurance? Are fifteen minutes on the web worth saving £5 on a book? Is an hour spent shopping in the high street worth saving £10 a year on an energy-efficient fridge? The easier it is made to save the more people will respond, hence the development of selling services, like insurance, travel and banking, over the phone or web. It avoids the chore of visiting shops or phoning around. It also, most crucially, saves consumers time (except when you are put on hold or web connections are slow!).

Consumers can also use the phone (and web) to save money on their energy bills by switching to a supplier who may give them a lower price and bundle all their services (electricity, gas, phone) together, which can be convenient. However, while this may save money it is unlikely to save energy, and may increase it since consumers may be tempted to increase their comfort levels as the energy now costs less – the so-called 'rebound effect' (see Section 3.5 below). However despite more than a decade of competition amongst suppliers and the ease of doing so, fewer than half of consumers have switched supplier (Ofgem, 2006).

There are also telephone services (and websites) that give advice on saving energy and being more energy efficient – local Energy Advice Centres. These have had some success. However, without a detailed home energy audit, their advice can only be general and falls into the following consumer-perceived categories:

1   The 'commonsense' – switch off lights not being used, turn the thermostat down, draw the curtains in winter.

2   Change in behaviour: showers instead of baths, driving more slowly.

3   Further action – visiting shops, getting quotations, applying for grants.

4   Not applicable to your circumstances – e.g. you don't own your home.

Thus it should be no surprise that consumers fail to take advantage of all the offers to save money (Ofgem, 2006). Firstly, they may not believe the offer. Secondly, they may think the offer is not relevant to them. Thirdly, they just haven't got the time to make the effort. Finally, for some people, there are more fun things to do in life than worry about saving £10, or even £50, a year.

3.2.3 Government concern

However one organisation that does worry about it is the government. It is concerned that market competition, economic productivity and getting something for less is a sign of efficiency and of competitive markets working to drive down costs. Consumers failing to take advantage of clear economic options is thus considered by some energy analysts as a sign of 'market failure' and the existence of 'market barriers'. There is, however, a wide-ranging debate over the exact nature of the 'market failure', of the 'barriers' to achieving a more economically efficient outcome, and what actions a government should take to remove 'market imperfections'.

Nevertheless policymakers promoting energy efficiency (and the present UK Government) believe there are substantial market barriers to people investing in energy efficiency. There is now an extensive academic literature on the nature of these barriers, drawn from a wide variety of disciplines:

institutional economics, management science, social psychology, sociology and political science (Sorrell et al., 2004).

A report from the Performance and Innovation Unit (PIU) says there is a broad consensus amongst energy-efficiency analysts and professionals on the key problem (PIU, 2001, paragraph 3.9).

Energy users in households and most businesses do not seek to optimise the economic efficiency with which they use energy. In a complex world, people have many concerns and most have a higher priority than energy efficiency. So projects that are primarily about energy efficiency are often not even considered. And in investment decisions and purchases that involve energy use, energy efficiency is usually a minor consideration. The PIU report identified barriers to investment in improving energy efficiency and the major points are listed in Box 3.2.

BOX 3.2 Market failure and the barriers to energy efficiency

The barriers to investment in improved energy efficiency may be described in a variety of ways, largely depending on the disciplinary background of the analyst. In neo-classical economic theory many are market failures. The following may be identified.

■ Most energy consumers have very imperfect information about energy efficiency opportunities and, especially in the domestic sector, may distrust information from vested interests;

■ Current market structures often require energy users to expend time and money to gather and assess information that is already available to suppliers;

■ Better information on capital costs than running costs leads to adverse selection of inefficient goods;

■ Capital markets are incomplete for many borrowers, for example low-income households cannot borrow even for very cost-effective projects;

■ Inadequate contractual relationships with builders and other traders result in 'moral hazard' in sub-optimal specifications and the risk that projects may not be implemented correctly;

■ Tenancy contracts and rental values provide split incentives for energy-efficiency investment in rented properties;

■ Household investment in energy efficiency has less beneficial fiscal treatment than corporate investment in energy supply, as taxation is based on income rather than profits;

■ Regulatory structures preclude potentially beneficial long-term contracts between licensed energy suppliers and domestic customers;

■ The price of energy, in most cases, fails to take into account the environmental costs associated with its supply and use, i.e. there are externalities.

PIU, 2001

The PIU report (paragraph 3.10) notes that to the vast majority of business and households, energy bills are a minor concern, averaging 3% of expenditure in households and only 1.3% in business. The only exceptions where energy costs are of importance are a few energy-intensive industrial users (steel, cement, chemicals, etc.) and households facing 'fuel poverty' (see Section 3.3.3).

The tendency of consumers to restrict their attention to only a number of issues is known in the academic literature as 'bounded rationality' (a concept first developed by economist H. Simon in his 1960 book *The New Science of Management Decision*). Consumers (like bureaucrats with an overflowing in-tray) have many issues competing for their attention, and it is to be expected that only the most important to them will be dealt with. The rest are put in the mental 'pending' tray, or if too troublesome, deliberately forgotten about.

The priorities of energy consumers are not the same as the priorities of energy-efficiency agencies, and as the PIU report admits (paragraph 3.11):

> It is clearly impractical for Government to seek to re-order the priorities of every energy user. The principal barrier to energy efficiency is therefore not easily open to 'correction'. Making energy use markets 'perfect' is therefore not a sensible goal. But this is not a case for inaction. The economic inefficiencies are large and a large number of policy interventions may improve them, even if they do not remove them. In the language of neo-classical economic theory, the policy options are 'second best', but they can still be a great deal better than no action at all.
>
> PIU, 2001

However, not all would agree. Many economists who dispute the existence of 'market barriers' would argue that any government action will only worsen market imperfections. Furthermore it could be argued that the imperfections in the energy-efficiency market are no worse than exist in other markets, such as insurance, food, housing, etc. and as such we have no more need of an Energy Efficiency Office than a Food Efficiency Office or a Travel Insurance Efficiency Agency.

This debate on the existence of market barriers and the need for government action is a complex one, often driven by political ideologies over the role of markets and government regulation. The question is what should the government do about what it perceives as the 'economic irrationality' of consumers. Should there be education campaigns to persuade them of the error of their ways (preaching), or should they be forced to change their minds through regulation and higher prices (the stick) or bribed through incentives and subsidies (the carrot)? Should we be more efficient through moral persuasion (it is good for us and good for the planet) or through economic self-interest (we can save money and spend it on luxuries)?

In the next section we examine the current UK Government policies on energy efficiency. Obviously to them and to agencies promoting energy efficiency these policies are very important, realistic and achievable. However when reading about them think about your own attitudes to saving money – how much effort would you make to save £50 or £10 a year? Do the policies, as the Government hopes, 'work with the grain' of real decision making?

3.3 Historic policies for energy efficiency

Over the last three decades the UK Government has explicitly promoted energy efficiency (or what was, in previous decades, termed 'energy conservation') with the aim of lowering the rate of growth of national energy use. This has been driven by various energy crises such as the oil price rises of 1973 and 1979, and now the prospect of future oil price increases. It has also been driven in the 1980s by the then Conservative government's policy to run down UK coal production, a battle which culminated in the coal miners' strike of 1984. Another current policy driver is the rise (in the 1990s) and current decline in UK natural gas production (see Figure 3.2).

However this desire for a reduction in energy demand has had to coexist with other policy aims that would tend to increase energy consumption, such as low energy prices and continued economic growth. The end result has been that economic growth has outpaced efficiency improvements, and UK national energy consumption has continued to increase (see Book 1, Figure 2.8).

3.3.1 Reasons for promoting energy efficiency

So does this mean that the UK Government should not promote energy efficiency? No, not at all; there are many valid and proven reasons to promote energy efficiency, as successive governments have done since the 1970s. Namely to:

1   encourage economic productivity and growth, and spur technical change, i.e. to encourage 'economic modernisation'

2   create export industries

3   help consumers adapt to higher energy costs

4   improve the housing stock and eradicate 'fuel poverty'

5   encourage fuel competition and keep down energy prices

6   reduce CO_2 emissions by reducing (fossil fuel) energy use.

These can be expanded on as follows:

(1) Economic modernisation

The first of these rests on successive governments' belief that government has a role to play in 'economic modernisation' and sponsoring research into new technologies. As the PIU Report comments (PIU 2001, paragraph 4.3):

> Most of the potential for future advance in energy efficiency will rely on technological improvements in materials technology, design and control. These are the types of change where the pace may accelerate in the knowledge economy. Energy efficiency is therefore expected to be an integral part of economic modernisation.
>
> PIU, 2001

This is a long-established policy, and has been implemented by specialist economic and technical agencies. Work on funding and disseminating

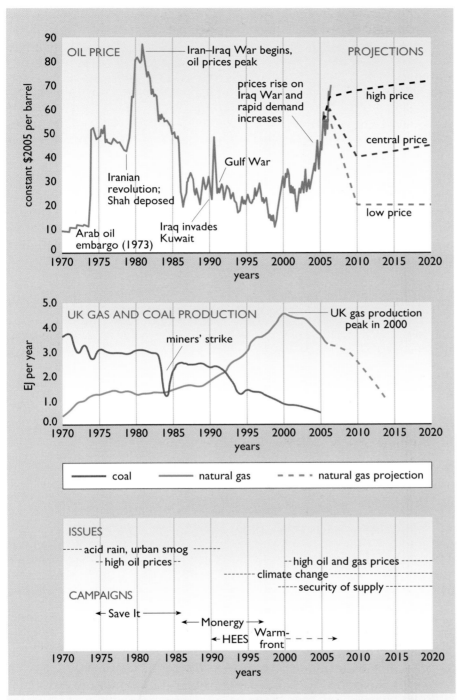

Figure 3.2 Timeline of energy issues and policies 1970–2020: (top) oil prices 1970–2006 and UK oil price projections 2005–2020; (middle) UK coal and natural gas production 1970–2005 and gas production projection 2005–2015; (bottom) issues and campaigns 1970–2020 (sources: oil price – USEIA, 2006. Oil price projection – DTI, 2006a. Coal and gas production – DTI, Energy in Brief (various); DTI, 2006a. UK natural gas production projections 2006–2014 – JESS, 2006)

the latest advances in energy efficiency were first carried out by the fuel industries (1950–70s) when they were nationalised industries, later in the 1970s by a specially created agency ETSU (the Energy Technology Support Unit) and then in the 1980s by the EEO (Energy Efficiency Office), followed in the 1990s by the EST (Energy Savings Trust) targeting the domestic consumer, and the Carbon Trust, targeting the commercial and industrial sector. Other research on energy efficiency is conducted by manufacturers of domestic appliances and cars, who play an important role in the setting of EU voluntary and mandatory labelling and standards schemes.

(2) Export industries

Some countries, such as Denmark, appear to have been more effective than Britain at creating exports for energy-efficiency products. The creation of successful export industries usually relies on a large domestic market for energy-efficient products, which can be stimulated by the imposition of national standards.

(3) To help consumers adapt

Governments have used various techniques to spread the energy conservation and efficiency message, initially to mitigate the impact of higher energy prices on consumers. These are:

(a) exhortation: involving publicity and awareness campaigns

(b) information: specific targeting of the message

(c) regulation: setting minimum standards

(d) taxation: proven to be very unpopular in the UK!

(e) incentives: giving grants or loans for investment.

(a) Exhortation

This involves press or TV advertising to a mass audience, generally domestic consumers, to create awareness of the problem with some very general advice and information on where to find further help. An early example was the 'Save It' campaign in the mid 1970s run by the UK Government (see below). More targeted advertising, like posters and leaflets, can then reinforce the message and provide sources of basic advice to the general public on ways to reduce energy use in the home, office or factory. Like all advertising the message must resonate with consumers if it is to be successful. This originally happened with the conservation message of 'Save It', but with the decline in the urgency of the 'energy crisis' of the 1970s (as North Sea oil and gas came into production) consumer attitudes changed and they became hostile or unreceptive to its message of conservation (see Section 3.3.2).

(b) Information

This involves targeting of the message, for example through energy information centres or telephone advice lines to answer specific questions from consumers. Another option is energy labelling of appliances and homes so that people can compare efficiencies and see the running cost. As described in Chapter 2, this has been done in the EU on domestic appliances since 1994, first with fridges and freezers and then extended to other household goods (washing machines, dryers, dishwashers, etc.), and is now being extended to buildings.

(c) Regulation

This is a long-standing way for governments to ensure minimum standards of energy performance. These can either be voluntary (agreed by manufacturers) or compulsory (set by law). In the UK, building standards have required certain levels of insulation in new homes since 1974 and these have progressively been upgraded, with the latest being in 2006. However by Continental European standards UK insulation levels are low.

In the USA there have been compulsory energy standards for domestic appliances since 1989 and voluntary standards for office equipment (the Energy Star Office Products program) from 1992.

In the EU there are voluntary standards for some appliances, but increasingly mandatory standards are being introduced, with minimum efficiency standards introduced for refrigerators in 1999 (see Chapter 2).

(d) Taxation

Energy taxation has proved unpopular with consumers and many governments committed to 'low taxation' policies. In the UK, while petrol and diesel for vehicles have always been heavily taxed (see Book 1, Chapter 12), domestic fuels only have a reduced 5% VAT rate, and attempts by the last Conservative Government in 1994 to raise the rate to the standard 17.5% proved very unpopular and were defeated. Similarly, massive protests in September 2000 by hauliers about high fuel prices, perceived to be due to increasing fuel taxes, resulted in the UK Government abandoning its policy of annually raising fuel taxes (see Book 3, Chapter 1).

Carbon taxes were first introduced in 1990 in Finland, closely followed a few years later by the other Scandinavian countries and then the Netherlands. They are most significant in Sweden, comprising a quarter of energy taxes but only 2–3% of total taxes. A 1992 proposal from the European Commission for a carbon/energy tax provided for the exemption of the six most energy-intensive industrial sectors, but even this concession was insufficient to stem industrial hostility based on fears of loss of competitiveness, and the proposed measure was dropped (Ekins and Barker, 2002). In the UK there is the Climate Change Levy which is a tax on energy use in the business and public sector (see Section 3.4 and Chapter 12 of Book 1).

(e) Incentives

These take the form of grants or low- or no-interest loans towards energy-saving measures or individualised energy advice (energy audits). For households, the most common measures are financial support for insulation schemes: loft insulation, draughtproofing, cavity wall insulation and heating system and controls upgrades. In the UK the government has been reluctant to subsidise the investments of most consumers, preferring to reserve its limited financial support for low-income consumers. Under the Home Energy Efficiency Scheme (HEES), the only universal grant was for loft insulation, available from 1978 to 1988 for all households and until 1990 for low-income households. From 1990 HEES grants for loft insulation and draughtproofing were given only to low-income or pensioner households, but there have been limited subsidies (or rebates) of a few million pounds for the purchase of energy-efficient compact fluorescent lamps (CFLs), fridges and condensing boilers. From June 2000, funding for HEES has been expanded, and it is now marketed as 'Warm Front'.

(4) Improve housing stock

The UK has some of Europe's worst housing conditions, hence the inability of many poor households to afford high heating standards. As noted in Chapter 2, the average English house would get only an E rating under the proposed Energy Labelling scheme. Energy efficiency improvements have been promoted as part of a package to upgrade the housing stock. The rate of improvement in insulation levels in the UK housing stock is limited by the very small (1% or less) rate of new build with its much higher levels of insulation. It is likely that two-thirds of the dwellings that will be standing in 2050 already exist. Thus to accelerate improved insulation levels it is important to concentrate on existing buildings. However, insulation grants have been minimal (see Section 3.3.3 on HEES below). Figure 3.3 shows that new housing can use less than a fifth of the space heating energy of the existing stock, and that improvements to the existing stock can lower energy use by a third. The main obstacle to further improvements is the cost of insulating solid walls. Insulation standards have nevertheless improved over the last few decades and it is estimated that domestic energy-efficiency measures have resulted in savings of 44% relative to what the consumption would have been without these measures (Shorrock and Utley, 2003, Table 27).

(5) Encourage fuel competition

Low energy prices have been the goal of all UK governments. First there was political control of energy prices by the nationalised industries, then after privatisation the use of regulation and encouragement of competition

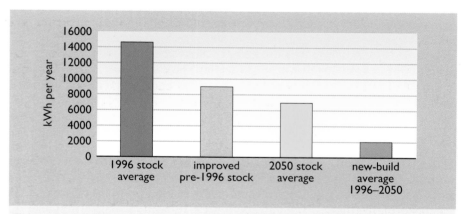

Figure 3.3 Housing annual space heating energy use by vintage 1996–2050 (source: Boardman et al., 2005)

amongst the privatised utilities. Fuel competition between electricity and gas utilities for the space and water heating market has also spurred efficiency improvements in new buildings and process heating equipment. However this competition is on the basis of cost, and the lowest cost fuel (such as off-peak electricity) may not produce the lowest (primary) energy consumption and CO_2 emissions.

(6) Reduce CO_2 emissions

From the 1990s successive governments have attached increasing importance to reducing national CO_2 emissions, and one way to achieve this is to lower national energy consumption. Hence the recent emphasis on energy efficiency as a way to reduce national energy use, and hence reduce emissions. This rests on the belief that promoting energy efficiency will lead to a real (or absolute) decline in national energy use, rather than just a reduction in the rate of increase.

3.3.2 Past government campaigns

Whilst the rationale for promoting efficiency remains constant, UK government campaigns on energy efficiency and conservation have changed over the past three decades, reflecting their immediate political concerns. Since the 1970s these campaigns have fallen into three categories:

1   to save energy: security of supply and depletion concerns

2   to save money: promoting economic efficiency and competitiveness

3   to save the earth: environmental concerns, especially global warming.

The first campaign was undermined by subsequent fossil fuel discoveries and enhanced oil and gas production techniques, the second by the decline in oil prices from 1986, but the third (and latest) is increasingly supported by the UK (and many other) governments.

Save It!

The first campaign in the 1970s to save energy was motivated by government concern over security of oil and coal supply. There was also a desire to conserve national energy resources for the future, when it was forecast that energy prices would be much higher. Thus the emphasis was on energy conservation, to stabilise, or even reduce, the absolute level of energy consumption.

The then Labour Government launched its conservation programme in January 1975 with the slogan 'Save It' (Figure 3.4), with such memorable hints on energy saving as 'have a bath with a friend', 'brush your teeth in the dark', etc. The public, faced with the reality of power cuts and imminent petrol rationing, responded well. It was a resonant message for many of the older generation who remembered similar calls during the Second World War when there was fuel rationing, and to some of the younger generation enamoured with the concept of 'self-sufficiency' and the need for alternative sources of energy. By the late 1980s, the 'energy crisis' had quickly passed (the miners went back to work and the OPEC embargo ceased) but the

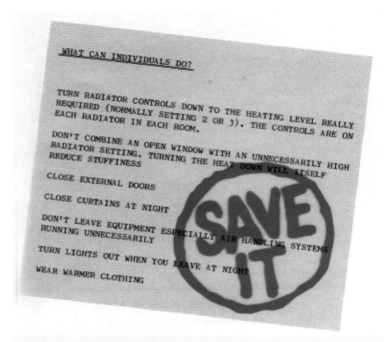

Figure 3.4 'Save it' leaflet produced by the UK government

image of energy conservation as that of voluntary restraint, simplicity and hardship persisted.

Historically the main reason for governments to promote energy savings was to conserve supplies at times of crisis. For example, the coal shortages experienced in much of Europe and Japan after the Second World War led to efforts by a number of countries to conserve stocks, often reducing supplies to households to ensure industry could get enough to maintain production. The other obvious example was the 1973 oil crisis, as a result of which many governments introduced a range of short- and long-term measures to promote better use of energy as a means of reducing dependence on imported oil (Owen, 1999)

During the 1970s the periodic scare that the world might run out of fossil fuels in the near future resurfaced again. Nowadays, apart from those convinced of the 'peak oil' theory, most economists believe that world reserves of fossil fuels will last for many decades but that they will start to become much more expensive owing to the greater demand from newly emerging economies, such as China and India (see Book 1, Chapter 7).

However with the end of the UK self-sufficiency in oil and gas, the government is becoming increasingly concerned about security of supply issues. It is placing its faith in liberalised global energy markets and seeking new energy supplies, particularly the import of liquefied natural gas (LNG) and the construction of new nuclear power stations (see DTI, 2006a, pp. 78–80).

Monergy

While one reaction to the 1970s 'energy crisis' was energy conservation, another was to look for new supplies of energy. This latter approach was boldly expressed in the United States by its Republican Presidents, Richard Nixon and later Ronald Reagan. As Nixon said in 1973:

> There are only seven per cent of the people in the world living in the United States, and we use thirty percent of all energy. That isn't bad; that is good. That means that we are the richest, strongest people in the world, and that we have the highest standard of living in the world. That is why we need so much energy, and may it always be that way.
>
> Hilgartner et al., 1982, p. 181

In contrast Jimmy Carter (Figure 3.5), the Democratic President from 1976–80, appealed to the American nation to embrace 'conservation', calling it the 'moral equivalent of war' (Horowitz, 2005). He was derided by Ronald Reagan, his rival candidate for the presidency who won by a landslide in 1980, and instead promoted energy production not conservation.

Similarly in the UK, Margaret Thatcher won the 1979 general election and emphasised energy production, particularly nuclear power. Policymakers quickly dropped the concept of 'conservation' and instead called for 'efficiency', which fitted in well with their free-market ideology of economic growth through using the greater efficiency of the private sector. Thus the second UK government campaign was based on saving money, not energy. So out went the 'Save It' campaign and in came the 'Monergy' campaign (see Figure 3.6), which stressed that energy efficiency was good for businesses, and boosted economic productivity.

Figure 3.5 President Carter in 1977 wearing a cardigan to illustrate his devotion to energy conservation

Saving the earth

The third and latest campaign, which has dominated energy-efficiency policy since the 1990s, seeks to reduce the environmental impact of energy production and consumption. Since the late 1980s global environmental concerns have risen up the political agenda, first with 'acid rain', then the 'ozone hole', and finally 'global warming'. One way to reduce CO_2 emissions was to reduce fossil fuel use, and energy efficiency has been increasingly promoted as the key solution (or technology) to reduce energy (or more particularly fossil fuel) consumption.

However, it is important to remember that global carbon emissions are not the only environmental impact from energy production and consumption, and that there are other important impacts at the local, national and regional level (see Book 1, Sections 13.5–13.6).

3.3.3 The Warm Front and Home Energy Efficiency Schemes

This ability of energy efficiency to entwine itself with other non-energy policies is clearly seen in the 'fuel poverty' debate, where it is promoted as the solution to enhancing heating standards amongst the 'fuel poor' – those households that would need to spend more than 10% of their income to achieve an 'adequate standard of warmth'. This problem can be seen in a variety of ways: as a social welfare issue (caused by inadequate incomes),

Figure 3.6 Monergy leaflet produced by the UK Government in the 1980s

a housing issue (caused by poor-quality housing) or an energy issue (poor insulation levels). The solutions are as varied as the causes: raising low incomes, insulating old housing, building new houses, or reducing energy prices.

The rather limited responses of past governments to this problem have been motivated more by government imperatives (or ideologies) rather than a clear social, fiscal or energy strategy. During the 1980s the Department of Energy provided only some limited financial support for home insulation schemes for low-income households run by local organisations, and managed nationally by Neighbourhood Energy Action (NEA). In 1991, in response to the campaigns of the fuel poverty lobbyists, HEES was created with an annual budget of £26m and again managed by NEA. HEES's funding was increased fourfold in 1994 to cover all those over 60, when the government introduced its politically sensitive proposal to raise the VAT rate on domestic energy to 17.5% (in the end the proposal was defeated but the HEES funding increase remained).

The current government's goal is to eliminate fuel poverty in the 'vulnerable' households that suffer from it by 2010. This would be achieved through energy-efficiency schemes (it relaunched HEES in 2000 with increased funding) and lower energy prices (also see Book 1, Chapter 12). Much progress was made: between 1996 and 2003 the number of vulnerable households in fuel poverty fell from around 5 million to around 1.5 million across the UK owing to improving housing standards, rising incomes and falling energy prices. However, rising energy prices from 2005 have reversed this downward trend and the number of vulnerable households in fuel poverty is expected to rise by around one million between 2004 and 2006.

While HEES may be an effective energy-efficiency scheme, however, it is a poor one for reducing energy demand. Research has found that, in low-income households, nearly all of the saving can be taken up in improved comfort (fewer draughts and higher temperatures), as previously most of these households could not afford to adequately heat their homes (Hong et al., 2006).

This very valid point – that it is the 'fuel rich' not the 'fuel poor' who can produce the most energy savings – illustrates the complexities and contradictions resulting from entwining energy efficiency with other non-energy policies. Measures which encourage energy efficiency and conservation, such as increased energy prices bought about by a higher rate of VAT on fuel, work against other policies such as alleviation of 'fuel poverty'. It is very hard to design energy policies that are fully compatible with other aspects of government policy. We all want, as the Prime Minister wrote in the 2006 *Energy Review* (DTI, 2006a), 'a sustainable, secure, and affordable energy supply' or in a nutshell – to have cheap energy with no adverse consequences. How far this is a feasible goal is debatable, as are the technical means to achieve it.

3.4 Current government policies

To reduce carbon emissions by 60% by 2050, the government estimates that energy use needs to fall by around 1.8% per year, but in recent years (2000–2005) energy demand in the domestic sector has continued to rise, albeit gently. This means we need a big increase – a step change – in the energy efficiency in our homes, if we are to achieve this target. The latest government policy, as expressed in the 2006 *Energy Review* (DTI, 2006a) states that such changes can be achieved in two ways:

- reducing the amount of energy that we need through technological improvements, for example to the structure of buildings so as to reduce the energy required for heating and cooling or to appliances so they require less energy; and
- changing our behaviour to reduce the amount of energy that we waste.

It therefore focuses on the following policies:

- raising energy-efficiency standards for new buildings and for the products we buy;
- encouraging a market for energy-efficiency services;
- providing the information, advice and support which stimulate us to improve energy efficiency and cut energy waste.

Thus making homes – both new homes and the existing housing stock – more energy efficient is the key to the government's policy. For new housing one approach is a series of demonstration projects. These include Northstowe, Cambridgeshire, where a new settlement of 10 000 homes aims to achieve a 50% reduction in energy use compared with conventional housing.

For appliances the government has identified several groups of products for action:

- domestic lighting
- consumer electronics such as set-top boxes, television sets and chargers
- white goods such as fridges, freezers and washing machines
- static electric motors and drives used in machinery such as pumps and fans (as used, for example, in air-conditioning systems)
- office equipment such as computers, printers and photocopiers.

Finally it aims to remove the least energy-efficient products from the market.

Home information packs

As noted in Chapter 2, energy performance certificates are to be introduced from June 2007 for most homes when they are bought or sold . These will rate the energy efficiency of a house on a scale of A to G. They will include information on the current average costs for the heating, hot water and lighting of the house, as well as practical advice on which energy-efficiency measures could be carried out.

Climate change levy

The UK business and public sector is subject to a tax on their energy use – the Climate Change Levy – designed to incentivise industry and the public sector to reduce their demand for energy. In order to protect the competitiveness of the most energy-intensive sectors of industry, Climate

Change Agreements (CCAs) were introduced as part of the Climate Change Levy package. Under these agreements, participating industries receive an 80% discount from the Climate Change Levy, provided that they enter into agreements to meet energy-efficiency targets or reduce their carbon emissions. CCAs currently run until 31 March 2013.

Local action

There are many barriers to individual engagement. Research has shown that engagement at a local and community level is important. This is because attitudes to climate change are more likely to be changed through individual interaction. Examples of organisations that will receive funding include the Scouts, who will be encouraging members to 'Be Prepared for the Future', and the Women's Institute who will develop EcoTeams (see Section 3.6.2) to help bring home the realities of climate change.

3.4.1 Potential for energy efficiency

New equipment and products are generally more energy efficient than older ones. This is all part of the trend of continual product improvement, whereby each new generation of equipment, by using the latest technologies, can provide the same energy service using less materials and energy. However, products often incorporate new features that provide a new range of services, and these often negate the energy savings – for instance, cars with air conditioning, frost-free fridges, TVs with standby, or larger homes with more bathrooms. Sometimes there is a radical shift in the technology which results in products that both have significant energy savings and better performance: compact fluorescent versus incandescent bulbs, microwave versus conventional cooking, laptops versus desktop computers, email versus postal service.

It must be borne in mind, however, that new technologies have different characteristics from older ones and not all consumers will find it convenient or desirable to use them, despite the obvious energy savings. For instance, some consumers prefer the soft yellow light of incandescent bulbs to the white light from fluorescent bulbs, meals baked in the oven taste different to those heated in the microwave, email doesn't have the romance of the letter, the open coal or wood fire is more cosy than gas central heating, etc.

There is a long history of some people rejecting modern technologies in favour of older ones, some because they can't afford the new ones (the rural poor), others because they prefer the old-fashioned lifestyle (the Edwardian country house fashion), and others who reject modern technology for political, ethical and religious reasons (hippies, the Amish). Technologies are often perceived as symbols of the economic and industrial structure that has produced them. People are far more likely to accept and use free CFLs given out by a local community group (such as EcoTeams or the Women's Institute) which they support, than from a remote utility with which they may have an antagonistic relationship. Thus it must be remembered that products and technologies are seldom 'value-free': the context in which they are promoted and distributed can crucially affect their uptake.

3.4.2 Assessing energy-saving potential

Table 1.14 in Chapter 1 shows that the domestic sector could halve energy and carbon emissions. This is a very significant potential, but how much could be achieved is a matter of dispute. It must be remembered that these are estimates, based on many assumptions, and it is highly unlikely that all these savings could be realised. Potential is rarely achieved. As the PIU report admits (paragraph 2.8), 'The fraction that can be achieved by 2010 is constrained by stock turnover, installer capacity and householder attitudes'. Nevertheless the UK Government is hopeful that current and future programmes will achieve annual savings of 4–6 MtC by 2020 or one-eighth of current domestic emissions of 40 MtC (see DTI, 2003, Table 2.1).

Similar types of analysis can be done for other sectors of the economy. In the service sector (commercial and public buildings) the economic potential is 22%, with technical potential nearly double that at 39% (see Section 1.5 of Chapter 1). In industry the economic potential is 24%, with the technical potential at 36%. Most of the potential lies in the energy-intensive industries, like steel, cement, paper, chemicals and engineering. In transport the estimated saving is one-third. Overall the PIU report (Table 4) estimates that nationally about 30% of energy could be saved, with consumers saving £12 billion a year

3.4.3 Stock turnover

It is most economic to make energy-efficiency improvements when the equipment, such as boilers or window frames, needs replacing. So the rate at which equipment wears out – termed 'stock turnover' – is crucial to the rate at which energy efficiency can be increased. However energy efficiency is usually a by-product of the design, as few appliances are purchased just because they are more energy efficient (exceptions, for example, are industrial motors and some chest freezers). Normally consumers face a limited choice, if any, of efficiencies in their purchases; for instance cars are offered in a wider variety of colours than efficiencies! However, the latest model of a refrigerator is likely be more efficient than previous versions because of regulatory standards.

There has been a continuous trend in improvements of energy efficiency in most energy services. Factor 4 or Factor 10 improvements are common for some products over a century. For instance there has been a Factor 10 improvement in lighting efficiency during the twentieth century as the early carbon filament bulbs have evolved (through technical progress and innovation) into the CFLs of today (see Section 9.3 in Book 1).

Also, as described in Chapter 1, there have been substantial improvements in the efficiency of domestic heating systems. Open coal fires with efficiencies of about 25% have been replaced with modern gas boilers with possible efficiencies of over 90%.

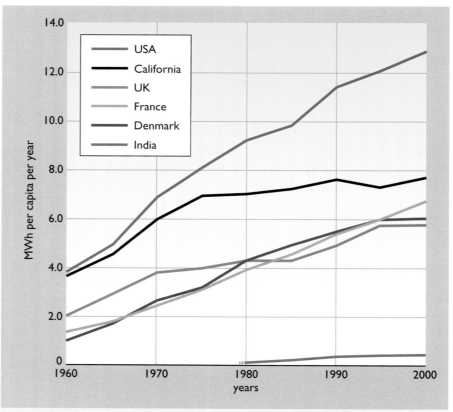

Figure 3.7 Per capita electricity consumption 1960–2000 for five countries (source: Smil, 1994) plus the State of California (source: Rosenfeld, 2003)

3.4.4 International comparisons

It is fairly easy to draw up rankings of countries by their energy intensities; what is more difficult is determining the reasons for the differences and the implications for energy efficiency. It is important to remember that energy indicators are just ratios, not explanations of energy efficiency. A low energy intensity or low use per capita need not indicate high energy efficiency. Look at the graph in Figure 3.7. This shows that the USA has double the electricity use per capita of European countries and more than ten times that of India. The reasons for this are partly due to differences in income per capita, but also due to weather and population density. One can also point to signs of a lavish lifestyle in the USA: large cars with a low number of miles per gallon (mpg), extensive homes with air conditioning, enormous refrigerators, frequent plane journeys and poor public transport.

However California, which has this lifestyle in abundance, also has the lowest electricity consumption per capita of any mainland state. Its state government has since the early 1980s been a leading promoter of energy efficiency, and has encouraged the use of low-energy lighting and efficient refrigerators and set performance standards for equipment such as computers.

So have California's energy-efficiency policies caused per capita electricity demand to grow much more slowly than the US average? Possibly, but this is a difficult problem in statistical analysis. There are a whole host of factors that affect growth in electricity use, such as growth in population, income, energy prices or changes in economic structure. Such questions are explored in work, for example, by Lee Schipper and his colleagues (Schipper and Meyers, 1992). One explanation for California's low-electricity use, however, is that it has a milder climate than most US states and thus uses little electricity for space heating and much less for air conditioning than other southern states, such as Texas. Another is that its state government is more willing than most states to implement energy-efficiency regulations, and these account for the slower rates of electricity consumption.

But is a high per capita consumption a sign of energy inefficiency? Is large inherently inefficient? What should be compared to what: a small to a large fridge, or the large US SUV to the British MINI? In other areas, such as manufacturing, the USA compares well in its energy efficiency to other countries (IEA, 1997). Is consumption just a feature of external national characteristics such as income (high in the USA), energy prices (low in the USA) and population density (low in the USA), rather than moral virtue or enthusiasm for energy efficiency? What is the linkage between consumption and efficiency? Do high levels of efficiency encourage, or even allow, high levels of consumption?

3.5 The rebound effect

The 'rebound effect' (or take-back effect) (see Figure 3.8) is the term used to describe the effect on consumption of an efficiency improvement, which by lowering the cost of producing or operating a product or service encourages people to use more of it. For instance when we replace a 75 W incandescent bulb with an 18 W compact fluorescent lamp (CFL) – a reduction in (wattage) power of about 75% – over time we could expect a 75% energy saving. However, there seldom is. Consumers realising that the light now costs less per hour to run are often less concerned about switching it off; indeed, they may intentionally leave it on all night. Thus they 'take back' some of the energy savings in the form of higher levels of energy service (more hours of light). This is particularly the case where the past level of energy services, such as heating, was considered inadequate. The energy savings from efficiency improvements, such as increased levels of insulation, may then be spent on much higher heating standards – the consumer benefits by getting a warmer home for the same or lower cost than previously. Finally, consumers may use new technologies in unexpected ways that increase energy use, rather than decrease it. For example in the 1970s it did not seem immediately likely that computers would become devices for home entertainment.

BOX 3.3 **Types of rebound effect**

There are three main types of rebound effect. First, the **direct rebound effect** is the increased use of energy services caused by the reduction in their price due to greater efficiency. This works exactly as would the reduction in price of any commodity and has immediate effects. Second, the **indirect effect** is caused by increased expenditure on other goods and services, due to the reduction in the cost of eco-efficient goods and services. For instance, some people might spend the savings from insulating their home on a foreign holiday! Third, the **economy-wide rebound effect** is the effect of efficiency changes on the direction and pace of technical change and innovation in the economy (Herring, 2005).

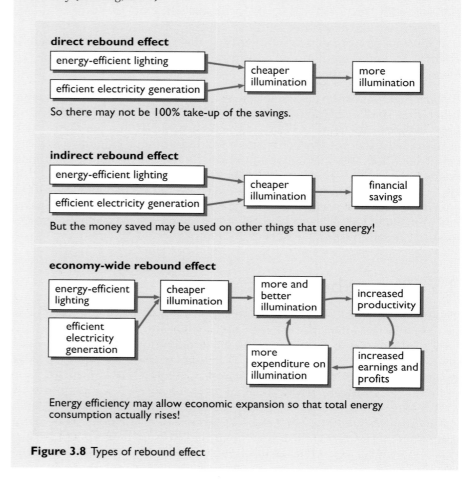

Figure 3.8 Types of rebound effect

3.5.1 **Seven centuries of lighting**

For lighting it is possible to track changes in efficiency and consumption over seven centuries, as has been done in a most fascinating study by Roger Fouquet and Peter Pearson (2006) for the UK. There they trace the evolution of demand for lighting as the technology of lighting progress, through medieval candles, 18th-century oil lamps, 19th-century gas lights and finally 20th-century electric lamps. Every time a new technology is introduced efficiency is improved and consumption increases dramatically. Our modern electric lights are 700 times more efficient than the oil lamps of 1800, and our consumption – measured in lumen-hours per capita – is over 6500 times greater. Even in the past 50 years, the era of the electric light, there has been a doubling of efficiency but a fourfold increase in consumption (see Table 3.1).

Table 3.1 Consumption of lighting, 1800–2000

Year	Price of lighting fuel /%	Lighting efficacy	Price of light per lumen-hour /%	Annual consumption (lumen-hours per capita)	Annual cost per capita of lighting	GDP per capita
1800	100%	1	100.0%	1	1.0	1.0
1850	40%	4	26.8%	4	1.1	1.2
1900	26%	7	4.2%	86	3.6	2.9
1950	40%	331	0.15%	1544	2.3	3.9
2000	18%	714	0.03%	6641	2.0	15.0

Index: 1800 = 1 (i.e. 100%)
Source: Fouquet and Pearson, 2006, Table 3

Over the last two centuries the real annual per capita cost for lighting (i.e. the 'real' price index times the annual consumption index) has doubled while GDP has increased by a factor of 15. So lighting has become much more affordable, and as we highly value illumination as an energy service it is not surprising that we consume so much more light.

3.5.2   Energy and economic growth

Energy-efficiency improvements by both consumers and producers initiate a chain of effects that have repercussions throughout the economy. The subject of the real costs of energy and its affordability was introduced in section 12.3 of Book 1. Increased energy efficiency in production reduces the cost of final outputs and makes consumption goods cheaper. Figure 3.9 shows how the real cost of electricity fell dramatically up to 1960, making a whole range of electrically powered activities and processes affordable. Most of this cost reduction was due to improvements in electricity generation and distribution technology. These new processes have in turn produced economic growth and increased real income for consumers, making increased energy consumption more affordable. Figure 3.10 shows the decline in energy prices relative to earnings, particularly those of gas and electricity, up to 2005.

At the same time, energy-efficiency improvements reduce production costs, increase producers' margins and increase production output. Higher margins may trigger a price war and encourage competitor firms to adopt energy-efficiency improvements. All these processes, as a result of these economy-wide rebound effects, encourage economic growth and, all else being equal, increase total energy demand. This acts to offset the original reduction in demand brought about by the efficiency improvements (Sorrell and Dimitripoulos, 2005).

The greatest effect (in the long term) of lower costs of energy services is most probably on the direction and pace of technical change and innovation in

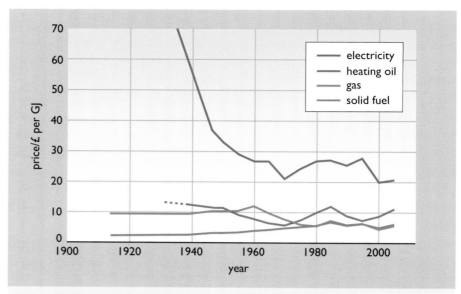

Figure 3.9 Real domestic energy prices in Great Britain 1914–2005 expressed in £(2000) (source: 1900–2000 updated from Evans and Herring, 1989; other data from DTI, 2006c)

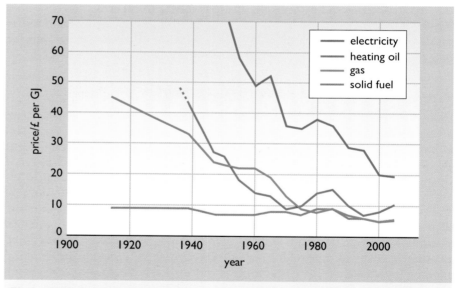

Figure 3.10 Domestic energy prices in Great Britain relative to earnings 1914–2005 expressed in £(2000) (source: 1900–2000 updated from Evans and Herring, 1989; other data from DTI, 2006c and National Statistics, 2006)

the economy, because new goods and services are created to take account of the possibility of lower energy costs. For instance, innovators and manufacturers – aware that the cost of lighting with CFLs has fallen by 75% – will devise new lamps for new lighting uses, like security or flood lighting, or for lighting previously unlit areas, such as the garden or patio. The market for lighting thus increases and consumption has increased by 50% in the last three decades. We may have energy-efficient lights but we have far more of them, and leave them on longer. Similarly with domestic appliances: they are getting more efficient but we own far more of them, so total energy consumption rises. In fact between 1972 and 2002, electricity consumed by them has doubled (EST, 2006a). However the new efficiency regulations on cold appliances are having an effect, with electricity consumption down since the late 1990s (see Figure 3.11).

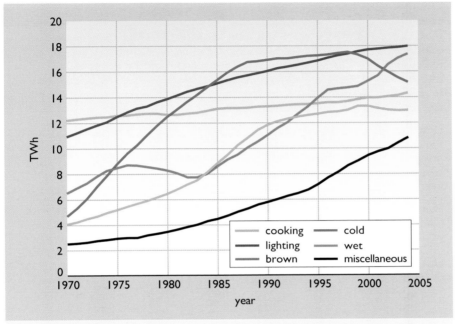

Figure 3.11 UK electricity consumption by type of domestic household appliance, 1970–2004. (source: DTI, 2006b)

Successive UK governments have made the improvement of insulation levels in housing a top priority, and while insulation levels have risen and appliances have become more efficient, total energy use in households has risen too. This was partly due to an increase in the number of households, but also due to higher heating standards (more widespread central heating systems and higher indoor temperatures) made feasible by insulation and boiler efficiency improvements. Energy is also so cheap, by historic standards, that we can afford to heat the outside air, with patio heaters! (See Figure 3.12.)

3.5.3 **Manufacturer and utility promotion**

Manufacturers and utilities often work closely together to market new appliances, though the emphasis is more on higher levels of energy services than on energy savings. Box 3.4 shows an early debate in the 1900s amongst manufacturers and utilities about the new tungsten filament bulb. As a result of this success, utilities have continually sought efficiency improvements in order to lower consumer costs and create new mass markets for their product, electricity. Furthermore, energy efficiency has been a useful marketing weapon against competing fuels, especially gas, in the lighting, heating and cooking markets.

Figure 3.12 Outdoor patio heaters

Electricity sales have grown as the efficiency of electricity generation has improved tenfold over the last century, and prices have fallen by over 90% in that period. The result is a mass market for electricity and the continual development of new electrical goods and services: electric lighting in the 1900s, domestic refrigeration in the 1930s, TV in the 1950s, microwaves and videos in the 1980s, computers and the internet in the 1990s.

BOX 3.4 Early 20th century lighting

In the early 1900s new light bulbs with tungsten filaments replaced those with carbon filaments. These new bulbs only used a quarter to a half of the electricity of the older bulbs. The immediate result for the electricity utilities, then heavily dependent on electric lighting sales, was a sharp drop in revenues. Some utilities responded to this loss of income by raising tariffs, and increasing the power of the bulbs.

However, the more far-sighted realised that this efficiency revolution allowed the creation of a mass market for electric lighting, and that it created the possibility of 'democratisation of electric lighting'. Instead of current tariffs based on low sales but high profit per unit of electricity sold, they argued for a tariff system based on lower profits per unit sold but greater sales.

The visionaries were proved right. Cheaper electricity combined with efficiency improvements created a mass market, much higher sales and greater profits. Electricity replaced gas for lighting, and the electricity revolution took off. Look again at the advert '20 hours for one penny' (Figure 1.34); this was part of this process of the 'democratisation of electric lighting', or lighting for the poor rather than just the wealthy.

3.6 Greater efficiency or less consumption?

The government's goal of a 60% reduction in CO_2 emissions by 2050 cannot be achieved just through energy-efficiency improvements. It also requires a shift to low-carbon energy sources. However it is hoped that energy-efficiency improvements will lead to an absolute reduction in energy consumption. Whether this is feasible is open to debate. It will certainly require a step change in the rate of efficiency improvements and in consumer behaviour.

3.6.1 Decoupling energy and economic growth

The historical record suggests it is very difficult to achieve such absolute reductions. Observations over the last 30 years have shown that:

- Most products are becoming more energy efficient due to a process of technical innovation.
- These products are slowly introduced into the economy by a process of 'stock turnover'.
- This does not mean they use less energy, as often we get products with more features (larger size, more power, etc.).
- Over time, developed economies grow faster than their energy consumption and consequently energy intensities decline.

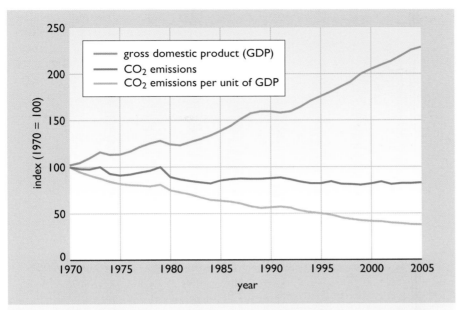

Figure 3.13 Trends in UK CO_2 emissions and GDP 1970–2005 (source: DTI, 2006b)

- The national economy is more 'energy efficient' but still uses more energy in absolute terms (due to economic growth).
- The only way economies have used less energy (i.e. an absolute decline) is for there to have been the painful combination of economic recession and industrial restructuring, and/or the export of energy-intensive industries.

One far-reaching goal proposed is to have both economic growth and an absolute decline in energy consumption – the Factor 4 approach (see Box 3.1). The UK Government believes that this complete decoupling of energy and economic growth is possible through the vigorous promotion of energy-efficiency policies, and points out that energy consumption has only risen by 15% since 1970 while economic output, as measured by GDP, has doubled (DTI, 2003, paragraph 2.16). There is also evidence of decoupling in respect of CO_2 emissions, which have declined 18% since 1970 while GDP has more than doubled (see Figure 3.13).

The UK Government's target for reducing CO_2 emissions is influenced by the many studies that argued that it was possible to achieve large reductions (of the order of 60%) in national CO_2 emissions, partly through reducing national energy consumption by a third to a half through energy-efficiency improvements (such as the RCEP scenarios described in Book 1, Box 1.4).

The degree to which energy efficiency might be taken up is dependent on a whole range of attitudes to energy. Figure 3.14 shows possible (and quite different) trends for residential carbon emissions under four 'Foresight Scenarios'. The Foresight programme was launched by the UK government in 1994 as a way of looking ahead and preparing for the future. Their four scenarios (see Box 3.5) are four broad views of how the future might turn out.

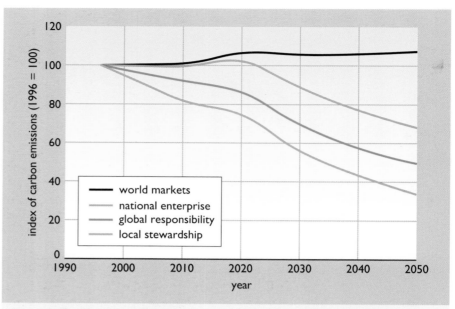

Figure 3.14 UK residential carbon emissions under the Foresight scenarios (source: Boardman et al., 2005, Figure 2.3)

BOX 3.5 The four 'Foresight Scenarios'

World markets

The UK electricity market continues to be dominated by fossil fuels, increasingly natural gas from Russia and Central Asia. Energy prices remain stable and there is little concern for energy security and energy efficiency. Renewable electricity generation technologies, such as wind power, become commercially viable but are not widely adopted due to low fuel prices and the low priority attached to climate change. Dependence on imports of transport fuels also grows significantly. There is a relatively slow diffusion of new power technologies like fuel cells.

National enterprise

Ensuring a supply of cheap and secure energy is the main objective of energy policy in this scenario. There is a drive to exploit domestic sources of energy, including domestic coal, gas and nuclear power by extending the lives of existing stations. The main driver for investments in energy efficiency and new and renewable sources of energy is energy security.

Global responsibility

Promoted for environmental as well as for economic reasons, natural gas is the dominant energy fuel up to 2010. Thereafter, renewable energy sources become fully commercial and gain a large market share. Dominant renewable sources are onshore and offshore wind, biomass, and solar energy. There is major infrastructure investment to support the use of hydrogen. Encouraged by regulatory incentives, energy suppliers move towards the provision of integrated energy services. New energy services as well as high energy prices greatly enhance the take-up of energy efficiency measures. The perceived need to reduce carbon emissions combined with a willingness to invest in technologies with low rates of return on capital revives a debate about nuclear power.

Local stewardship

Energy systems are diverse and are restructured around local energy resources, whether fossil or non-fossil fuel. A wide range of small-scale renewable energy technologies are exploited, particularly wind, biogas, biomass, and photovoltaics. Combined heat and power systems flourish. Many of the new technologies are subsidised through funds raised by substantial energy taxes. High energy prices lead to the adoption of energy efficiency measures and encourage consumers to save electricity. This trend, coupled with low economic growth, leads to an absolute fall of energy demand.

Source: DTI, 2002

Like all projections of the future these scenarios, on lower national energy consumption, are debatable but cannot be proven wrong, at least not until the date for which they are set (2050 for the RCEP and Foresight scenarios) arrives. But the overall historic record of forecasters is poor, and such scenarios should be treated more as 'learning tools' to indicate the sort of measures required, rather than statements of what is likely to occur (see Smil 2003, Chapter 3).

3.6.2 **Sustainable consumption**

The UK Government policy of energy efficiency is linked into its goal of sustainable development (see Book 1, Section 1.2). In turn sustainable development can be split into two areas: one on production, and the other on consumption. Sustainable consumption is composed of three elements:

- consuming more efficiently
- consuming differently
- simply consuming less.

Consuming more efficiently relies on the idea of improving 'resource productivity' or 'eco-efficiency'. The success of sustainable consumption (as a concept) so far has rested on the belief that it is easy to consume more efficiently or achieve 'Factor 4', by using energy and resources more productively. However while resources may be used more efficiently, it does not mean that less of them are used.

The second plank of sustainable consumption is to consume services rather than goods, based on the idea that services consume less resources than products. Again the use of services rather than products does not necessarily mean lower use of resources, particularly if it involves higher standards of services or the extensive use of transport, or other infrastructure such as telecommunications networks, to deliver the service (e.g. home deliveries of internet shopping or takeaway meals).

The most contentious aspect of sustainable consumption is about consuming less, as it requires us to examine our lifestyle and question our consumption patterns. Even if we are prepared to acknowledge that our 'quality of life' is not really about material consumption, it is very hard for most of us to give up our possessions, reduce our shopping, or to cut down our consumption of resources generally. We can always rationalise and give good practical reasons for our consumption: we need a car because there is no bus to work and it is so much more convenient; we need to fly abroad for holidays because it is cheaper and sunnier than staying at home; we all want to do our bit for the environment but only if it costs little, saves us money and is convenient. As a recent report from the Royal Society remarks:

> Unsurprisingly, the concept of sustainable consumption is not popular with governments. It wins few votes and provides an implied threat to competitiveness, employment and profitability. Instead citizens are encouraged to spend, spend and spend.
>
> Heap and Kent, 2000, p. 1.

So is spending and consuming less an option? Can people change their behaviour towards less material and energy consumption?

Changing behaviour

There are already well-established regulatory approaches to reducing energy consumption, like energy taxes, building regulations, and even rationing in emergencies. What of the behavioural approach: are people willing to reduce their consumption? The answer seems to be 'yes' if it is a group activity (SCR, 2006). A poll for the BBC (see Box 3.6) found that most people – 85% – said they were willing to make some behavioural changes to tackle climate change, but two-thirds were unwilling to pay more for petrol.

BOX 3.6 **BBC poll on climate change and consumption**

[In a poll for the BBC in July 2004] climate change came last of the list of important issues facing the UK, chosen by 53%, though 64% said it was one of the most important problems facing the world. ... Asked whether changes in personal behaviour would make a difference, 54% said yes and 44% no. Despite that, 85% said they would be prepared to make changes, with only 13% dissenting. The changes people were prepared to make included recycling more household waste (96%), using less energy at home (92%), using cars less (68%), and taking fewer flights (62%). But only 51% said they would be prepared to pay more to fly, and just 37% would agree to pay more for petrol.

Kirby, 2004

Recent research reveals that the vast majority (93%) of consumers are in favour of tougher product regulations and consumer incentives to purchase energy-efficient goods. And half of consumers would like a ban on the least energy-efficient domestic electrical appliances (EST, 2006b).

However, adopting more efficient (or greener) products without reducing the growth in consumption will not make a large difference in the long term. Research by Eva Alfredsson shows that while adopting green consumption patterns can produce a reduction in energy in the short term of 10% to 20%, these reductions are soon outpaced due to rising levels of consumption, caused by even modest growth (1% to 2% per annum) in income (Alfredsson, 2004).

Figure 3.15 A GAP EcoTeam shares ideas

Ecoteams approach

It is much easier to change your behaviour if you are part of a group, which provides encouragement and support. In Section 2.10 in Chapter 2 of Book 2 you read about the small groups promoting DIY solar water heaters in Austria. Similarly there are such self-help groups promoting energy efficiency. For instance Global Action Plan (GAP), an environmental charity, adopts a collective, community-based strategy called the EcoTeam approach. This is a group of six to ten people who might be neighbours, members of the same religious organisation or of some interest group or club (see Figure 3.15). They meet once a month and their eight-month programme is based on a workbook which addresses six areas in turn: waste, gas, electricity, water, transport and consumption. The emphasis is on the household rather than the individual, so that EcoTeam members work with other household members to change behaviour.

The most detailed evaluation of the EcoTeams approach was in the Netherlands, where it was found that EcoTeams have typically achieved reductions in car use and consumption of energy and water of around 10%, and reductions in waste of around 40%, with similar results being achieved in Britain. It was found that participants were most likely to maintain behaviour changes if they were motivated by a strong and positive link to personal meaning and identity.

Personal carbon allowances

The experiences of such groups as Global Action Plan in achieving behavioural changes would be important if the UK Government ever introduced radical measures such as a personal carbon allowance, whereby all citizens would be given equal carbon allowance and issued with a 'Carbon allowance' card (see Figure 3.16). People who take measures to cut the pollution they produce could sell their surplus. Those who continue to produce pollution above their personal cap would have to buy credits on the open market.

In a speech in July 2006 David Miliband, the UK environment secretary, said:

> ... we should look more radically at the option of tradable personal carbon allowances. Imagine a world where carbon becomes a new

Figure 3.16 A possible carbon allowance card of the future

currency. We all carry carbon points on our bank cards in the same way as we carry pounds. We pay for electricity, gas and fuel not just with pounds but carbon points

(Adam, 2006)

He is keen to set up a pilot scheme to test the idea, and has asked officials from four government departments to report on how it could be done.

Personal carbon allowances would cover all direct use of energy by individuals, which accounts for 44% of national carbon emissions. This includes all household and personal transport energy use including air travel. There would be an equal carbon allowance for all adults, and those people who invest in household efficiency and renewables, travel less, and who lead lives with a lower energy input would not need all of their allowance and would therefore have a surplus to sell. Those who travel a lot, or who live in large or inefficient homes would need to buy this surplus to permit them to continue with something like their accustomed lifestyle. Thus people could trade carbon, and trading would be an integral part of a carbon allowance scheme.

The carbon allowances would gradually decrease over time, in response both to the need to reduce global emissions and to allow for the expected rise in national population. This would have severe consequences for international travel, since for example just one return flight from London to Athens could exceed the whole personal carbon allowance for the year in 2030 (Hillman and Fawcett, 2004).

For such a policy to work there would have to be extensive information given to consumers on the carbon content of all goods and services they purchase, and the existence of alternatives to carbon-intensive activities like flying. You may think carbon allowances unrealistic in our age of consumer choice and freedom, but it is being taken increasingly seriously by politicians and policymakers, and may be a necessary measure in the future where there is rapid climate change requiring drastic and rapid cuts in global carbon emissions.

3.6.3 What role for energy efficiency?

In the UK over the past 50 years, primary energy consumption has nearly doubled despite great improvements in energy efficiency (see Book 1, Figure 2.8). This suggests that we prefer to take much of our (money) savings in efficiency in the form of higher levels of energy service, such as using central heating or having larger fridges, rather than reduced consumption. This is not surprising since the effect of increased efficiency is to lower the implicit price of an energy service, and hence make its use more affordable to existing and new consumers. While appliance standards make goods more efficient, our growing economy allows us to have more of them. Hence in this race between energy efficiency and economic growth, energy consumption has not fallen.

The overall impact of efficiency standards has been mixed. While standards seem to be having an impact on wet and cold appliances (see Figure 3.12), the *40% House* Report commented:

> However, such advances are not expected to be sufficient to completely offset the increase in overall consumption due to population and appliance ownership trends. The average size of cold appliances on the market increased by 15% between 1995 and 2001, reducing the impact of efficiency improvements. The efficiency gains have also been negated to a certain extent by unregulated growth in consumer electronics sector, where the trend appears to be towards higher rather than lower energy use (e.g. plasma TVs and the digital revolution).
>
> Boardman et al., 2005, p. 50

There is considerable scope to introduce more energy-efficiency regulations. Below is an illustrative list of the types of measure that have worked effectively already (whether in the UK, EU or elsewhere) and which could form part of a future UK products policy (EST, 2006a, p. 36):

- Mandatory product standards in new-build homes. Requirements on housing developers to install only the most efficient appliances (where the home is sold with appliances) and dedicated CFL fittings.
- Accelerated and sustained tightening of product standards.
- Minimum standards for standby power consumption.
- Voluntary and binding agreements with retailers, especially for consumer electronics.
- Tax on inefficient products. e.g. incandescent bulbs could be taxed at a rate of at least 50p per unit, and also on 'luxury' products which have a disproportionately high environmental impact in relation to their utility (e.g. outdoor patio heaters).
- Outright bans of products. This has already proved successful, e.g. for inefficient refrigerators.

Again the idea of banning inefficient products may seem too radical, but in a speech in July 2006 David Miliband did suggest banning products such as inefficient light bulbs and electrical appliances that waste power while on standby (Adam, 2006). He also suggested new environmental taxes to shift the cost of carbon pollution onto consumers and proposed that consumers might make automatic payments to offset their pollution.

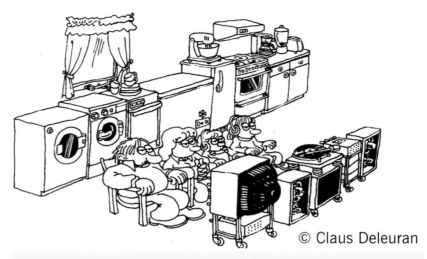

© Claus Deleuran

Figure 3.17 A vision of the 'good life' of the 1990s

What is the 'good life'?

Ultimately the key questions are ethical not technical, cultural rather than economic. What is the 'good life'? Can we consume more goods and services (for a higher quality of life) but use less materials and energy? Can a low(er)-energy lifestyle be made desirable by moral suasion or cultural example? Is the good life one of owning a lot of appliances, to make our life easier so we can slump in a chair and be entertained with the latest electronic gadgets (see Figure 3.17)?

Or are appliances a means to the good life, an enabling technology that helps us achieve non-material goals? Look again at Figure 1.34 – '20 hours for one penny' and contrast the family in this images from a century ago with that above for the 1990s. The electric light bulb was definitely a liberating and enabling technology; can you say the same for the plasma TV? At what stage do we say we have enough energy? We are being urged to accept a 60% reduction in our CO_2 emissions. This will undoubtedly require us to use less energy. As the energy analyst Vaclav Smil so passionately argues:

> Such reductions would call for nothing more than a return to levels that prevailed just a decade, or no more than a generation, ago. How could one even use the term sacrifice in this connection? Did we live so unbearably 10 or 30 years ago that the return to those consumption levels cannot be even publicly contemplated by serious policy makers because they feel, I fear correctly, that the public would find such a suggestion unthinkable and utterly unacceptable?
>
> Smil, 2003, p. 338

The call to return to lower consumption levels asks us to devise a policy of energy 'sufficiency' – that is, living well on less energy. This new 'conservation' lifestyle will take time and requires much political consensus and many practical solutions. It will require that we need to decouple economic growth from energy consumption. This needs, as we all acknowledge, a step change in the rate of energy-efficiency improvement, something we have seldom, if ever, achieved. Energy efficiency is a key tool in this quest to achieve sufficiency, but the end result will depend on how we use it.

References and Further Reading

Adam, D. (2006) 'Swipe-card plan to ration consumers' carbon use', *The Guardian* 19 July.

Alfredsson, E. (2004) '"Green" consumption – no solution for climate change', *Energy* vol. 29, no. 4, pp. 513–24.

Boardman, B. Darby, S., Killip, G., Hinnells, M., Jardine, C., Palmer, J. and Sinden, G. (2005) *40% House*. Oxford, Energy Change Institute; http://www.40percent.org.uk/ [Accessed 10 December 2006].

Cooper, T. (2005) 'Slower Consumption: Reflections on Product Life Spans and the "Throwaway Society"', *Journal of Industrial Ecology*, vol. 9, pp. 1–2.

Department for Environment, Food and Rural Affairs (DEFRA) (2004) *Fuel Poverty In England: The Government's Plan for Action*, London, DEFRA; also available online at http://www.defra.gov.uk/environment/energy/fuelpov/pdf/fuelpov_actionplan.pdf [Accessed 1 September 2006].

Department of Trade and Industry (DTI) (various) *Energy in Brief*, London, DTI; also available online at http://www.dti.gov.energy [Accessed 11 October 2006].

Department of Trade and Industry (DTI) (2002) *Foresight futures 2020: revised scenarios and guidance*, London, DTI; also available online at http://www.foresight.gov.uk [Accessed 15 December 2006].

Department of Trade and Industry (DTI) (2003) *Energy White Paper: A Summary – Our energy future – creating a low carbon economy*, London, DTI; also available online at http://www.dti.gov.uk/files/file10723.pdf?pubpdfdload=03%2F658 [Accessed 1 Sept 2006].

Department of Trade and Industry (DTI) (2006a). *The Energy Challenge: Energy Review*, London, DTI; also available online at http://www.dti.gov.uk/energy [Accessed 1 September 2006].

Department of Trade and Industry (DTI) (2006b) *Energy Sector Indicators 2006*, available from www.dti.gov.uk/energy [Accessed 29 June 2006].

Department of Trade and Industry (DTI) (2006c) *Quarterly Energy Prices*, London, DTI; also available from www.dti.gov.uk/energy [Accessed 15 December 2006].

Ekins, P. and Barker, T. (2002) 'Carbon taxes and carbon emissions trading' in Hanley, N. and Roberts, C.J. (eds) *Issues in Environmental Economics*, Oxford, Blackwell.

Energy Savings Trust (EST) (2006a) *The rise of the machines: a review of energy using products in the home from the 1970s to today*. London, Energy Savings Trust; also available online at http://www.est.org.uk/uploads/documents/aboutest/Riseofthemachines.pdf#search=%22EST%20rise%2 0of%20the%20Machines%22 [Accessed 1 September 2006].

Energy Savings Trust (EST) (2006b). 'Consumers demand ban on most inefficient products' [online], Press release 3 July, London, Energy Savings Trust, http://www.est.org.uk/aboutest/news/pressreleases/index.cfm?mode=view& press_id=518 [Accessed 1 September 2006].

Evans, R.D. and Herring, H. (1989) *Energy Use and Energy Efficiency in the Domestic Sector up to the year 2010*, Energy Efficiency Office, HMSO.

Fawcett, T. (2004) 'Carbon Rationing and Personal Energy Use', *Energy & Environment*, vol. 15 , no. 6, pp. 1067–84.

Fouquet, R. and Pearson. P. (2006) 'Seven Centuries of Energy Service: The price and use of light in the United Kingdom (1300–2000)'. *The Energy Journal*, vol. 27, no. 1, pp. 139–176.

Heap, B. and Kent, J. (eds) (2000) *Towards Sustainable Consumption: a European Perspective*, London, The Royal Society.

Herring, H. (2005) 'Energy Efficiency: A Critical View', *Energy*, vol. 31, no. 1, pp. 10–20.

Hilgartner, S., Bell R. and O'Connor, R. (1982) *Nukespeak: Nuclear Language, Visions And Mindset*, San Francisco, Sierra Club Books.

Hillman, M. and Fawcett, T. (2004) *How we can save the planet*, London, Penguin.

Hounsham, S. (2006) *Painting the Town Green: How to persuade people to be environmentally friendly*. London, Green-Engage/Transport 2000; also available online at http://green-engage.co.uk/project_painting.html [Accessed 10 December 2006].

Hong, S., Oreszczyn, T., Ridley, I. and the Warm Front Study Group (2006). 'The impact of energy efficient refurbishment on the space heating fuel consumption in English dwellings', *Energy and Buildings*, vol. 38, no. 10, pp. 1171–81.

Horowitz, D. (2005) *Jimmy Carter and the Energy Crisis of the 1970s*. New York, Bedford/St Martins.

International Energy Agency (IEA) (1997) *Indicators of Energy Use and Efficiency: Understanding the link between energy and human activity*, Paris, IEA; also available online at http://www.iea.org/Textbase/publications/free_new_Desc.asp?PUBS_ID=1163 [Accessed 1 September 2006].

Joint Energy Security of Supply Working Group (JESS) (2006) *Sixth Report*; also available online at http://www.dti.gov.uk/energy/reliability/security-supply/jess/index.html [Accessed 11 October 2006].

Kirby, A. (2004) 'Britons unsure of climate costs', BBC News Online, 29 July http://news.bbc.co.uk/1/hi/sci/tech/3934363.stm [Accessed 18 December 2006].

Levett, R., Christie, I., Jacobs, M. and Therivel R. (2003) *A Better Choice of Choice: Quality of Life, Consumption and Economic Growth*. London, Fabian Society.

National Statistics (2006) *Annual Earnings Index*, available from http://www.statistics.gov.uk [Accessed 15 December 2006].

Office of Gas and Electricity Markets (Ofgem) (2006) *Domestic Retail Market Report* [online], Report 110/06, London, Ofgem, http://www.ofgem.gov.uk/temp/ofgem/cache/cmsattach/15610_DRMR_March_2006.pdf [Accessed 1 September 2006].

Owen, G. (1999) *Public Purpose or Private Benefit? The Politics of Energy Conservation*, Manchester, Manchester University Press.

Performance and Innovation Unit (PIU) (2001) *Energy Efficiency Strategy*, UK Cabinet Office, http://www.strategy.gov.uk/downloads/files/PIUc.pdf [Accessed 1 September 2006].

Parliamentary Office of Science and Technology (POST) (2005) *Household Energy Efficiency*, POST, Report No. 249, October, http://www.parliament. uk/documents/upload/postpn249.pdf [Accessed 1 September 2006].

Princen, T., Maniates, M. and Conca, K. (eds) (2002) *Confronting Consumption*, MIT Press.

Royal Commission on Environmental Pollution (RCEP) (2000) *Energy -- The Changing Climate*, London, The Stationery Office, http://www.rcep. org.uk/newenergy.htm [Accessed 1 September 2006].

Rosenfeld, A.H. (2003) *The California Vision, Reducing Energy Intensity 2% per year*, California Energy Commission.

Schipper, L. and Meyers, S. (1992) *Energy Efficiency and Human Activity: Past Trends, Future Prospects*, Cambridge, Cambridge University Press.

Sustainable Consumption Roundtable (SCR) (2006). *I Will if you Will: Towards Sustainable Consumption*, http://www.sd-commission.org.uk/ publications.php?id=367 [Accessed 1 September 2006].

Shorrock, L.D. and Utley, J.I. (2003) *Domestic energy fact file*. BRE Bookshop.

Shorrock, L.D., Henderson, J. and Utley, J.I. (2005). *Reducing carbon emissions from the UK housing stock*, BRE Bookshop.

Simon, H. (1960) *The New Science of Management Decision*, New York, Harper.

Smil, V. (1994) *Energy in World History*, Westview Press, Boulder, Colorado.

Smil, V. (2003) *Energy at the Crossroads*, MIT Press.

Sorrell, S., Schleich, J., Scott S. and O'Malley, E. (eds) (2004). *The Economics of Energy Efficiency: Barriers to Cost Effective Investment*. Cheltenham, Edward Elgar.

Sorrell, S. and Dimitropoulos J. (2005) *An assessment of evidence for a 'rebound effect' from improvements in energy efficiency*, Scoping Note, SPRU, University of Sussex, October 2005. http://www.ukerc.ac.uk/ content/view/130/187 [Accessed 1 September 2006].

US Energy Information Administration (USEIA) (2006) *Annual Oil Market Chronology* [online] http://www.eia.doe.gov/emeu/cabs/AOMC/Overview. html [Accessed 11 October 2006].

Weizsacker, E. von, Lovins, A.B. and Lovins, L.H. (1997) *Factor Four: Doubling Wealth – Halving Resource Use*. Earthscan.

Acknowledgements

Chapter 1

Grateful acknowledgement is made to the following sources:

Tables

Table 1.8: Adapted from 'Good Practice Guide GPG310 Degree Days for Energy Management – a practical introduction', The Carbon Trust; Table 1.14: Adapted from 'Energy Efficiency Strategy' (2001), Performance and Innovation Unit, UK Cabinet Office.

Figures

Figures 1.1, 1.2 and 1.3: DTI, 'Energy Consumption in the UK'. From www.dti.gov.uk/energy/statistics/publications/energy-consumption/page17658.html. Crown copyright material is reproduced under Class Licence Number C01W0000065 with the permission of the Controller of HMSO and the Queen's Printer for Scotland; Figures 1.8 and 1.9: © The Energy Saving Trust 2005; Figures 1.15 and 1.36: Nicholls, R. (2002) Low Energy Design, p. 42, Interface Publishing; Figures 1.19 and 1.20: Courtesy of Luwoge; 1.27: Courtesy of Cogenco Ltd.; Figure 1.29: DTI, 'Energy Consumption in the UK.' Crown copyright material is reproduced under Class Licence Number C01W0000065 with the permission of the Controller of HMSO and the Queen's Printer for Scotland; Figure 1.31: Courtesy of www.sxc.hu/photo/189970/lotushead; Figure 1.33: Reprinted from Energy: Management, Supply and Conservation, 2006, Beggs, C., 'Energy efficient electrical services' p.239, Copyright 2002, Clive Beggs, with permission from Elsevier; Figure 1.34: © Mary Evans Picture Library; Figure 1.37: Reprinted from Energy: Management, Supply & Conservation, 2006, Beggs, C.,' Passive solar and low energy building design', p. 267, Copyright 2002, with permission from Elsevier; Figure 1.43: Courtesy of University of East Anglia.

Every effort has been made to contact copyright holders. If any have been inadvertently overlooked the publishers will be pleased to make the necessary arrangements at the first opportunity.

Chapter 2

Figures

Figure 2.4: Courtesy of Dr Jez Wingfield, Leeds Metropolitan University; Figure 2.6: Adapted from ' Energy Consumption Guide 19' by Energy Efficiency Best Practice Programme from www.energy-efficiency.gov.uk.

Chapter 3

Figures

Figure 3.1, 3.3 and 3.14: Boardman B. et al. (2005) 40% House, Environmental Change Institute, University of Oxford; Figures 3.4 and 3.6: 'Save it', mid 1970s and 'Monergy' late 1970s. Crown copyright material is reproduced under Class Licence Number C01W0000065 with the permission of the Controller of HMSO and the Queen's Printer for Scotland; Figure 3.5: 'A Chat By The Fireside', Time Life Pictures, © Getty Images; Figure 3.13: Copyright © Stephen Williams; Figure 3.11: DTI (2006) UK Energy Sector Indicators 2006. Crown copyright material is reproduced under Class Licence Number C01W0000065 with the permission of the Controller of HMSO and the Queen's Printer for Scotland; Figure 3.13: DTI (2006) UK Energy Sector Indicators 2006. Crown copyright material is reproduced under Class Licence Number C01W0000065 with the permission of the Controller of HMSO and the Queen's Printer for Scotland; Figure 3.15: Janine Wiedel Photolibrary / Alamy Images; Figure 3.17: © Claus Deleuran/ DACS 2006.

Authors' acknowledgement

The authors would like to thank the following for their assistance in preparing this book:

Godfrey Boyle

Janet Ramage

Robin Roy

Jeremy Harrison, Powergen Ltd

David Olivier, Energy Advisory Associates

Professor Bob Lowe, Bartlett School of Architecture

Steve Smith, Whispergen Ltd.